D1096145

SHORT STORY
SMORGASBORD

by

ROBERTS WHITCOMB LAING

Dedication

to the first 86 years of
the 20th century, which have
give me so much, In fact
they make me want to see the
next twenty – just to see
what the hell happens next.
(Also used in Phase II)

Printed in the United States of America

 **PINE HILL PRESS**
Freeman, S. Dak. 57029

CONTENTS

Roberts Whitcomb Laing

Preface
About the Author

Roberts Whitcomb Laing, born in Alliance, Nebraska, April 4, 1907 to Cyrus A. and Mary E. Laing, had a varied an interesting life only a small portion of which had much to do with authorship. Writing the *Great American Novel* was not to be his privilege or lot.

Soon after passing through the phase of aspiring to be a cowboy, a fireman or a locomotive engineer, he became captivated with music. There was no music program then in Alliance schools, so he was started with private music lessons and probably would have wound up playing the piano had not his teacher had a bad case of halitosis.

That was hard for Mother Laing to believe until his objections resulted in an outright refusal to continue the lessons. However, after she checked the situation herself, by sitting on the piano bench through a lesson, she was convinced about the bad breath and the piano lessons became a memory.

Dad Laing, who had a leaning for brass bands, *helped* the boy decide on the trombone. He learned to play that horn with a few lessons from the town's band master, who played the cornet, and also, by sitting in the city band next to a veteran *slip-horn* player, reputed to have played in Sells Flota circus bands. Soon he was playing in local bands and for the next ten years, orchestras provided a second income putting him through the University of Nebraska and providing travel experience from Seattle, Washington, over most of the states of Nebraska, Kansas, some of South Dakota and abroad to Paris, Jerusalem, Cairo and other interesting places.

At one time, the young man considered a big band leader career, but that never developed as debt incurred by finishing college and responsibility to the home folks, won out over the glitter of the ballrooms.

In 1930, he took a job in a local bank. It had a much more solid future and some little prestige for the next seven years, when he was enticed by the local municipal officials to become the city's clerk and finance director. Alliance had its own power generating plant and utility system, which justified the latter title and made the position worthwhile financially. After the next ten years, of being more-or-less second in command and learning the difference between a kilowatt and a pianissimo under the influence of the then city manager, "R. W." was appointed Alliance City Manager in 1947 and served in that capacity for the next 25 years, retiring in 1972.

Those were golden ones for his ego and status. In the World War II post war years, elected councilmen were busy with their own affairs and businesses. Once he had won their confidence, he pretty much was given his head. He admits that he was spoiled with authority, but it was comforting to be dubbed *a benevolent dictator* by his remarkably few critics. The electric utility, the city's biggest single asset, was healthy and the City Counselor once best expressed some of the reason for that by saying, "My boss runs a tight ship."

In the state picture, Alliance was the envy of many of the *have not* communities. Laing served as president of the Nebraska League of Municipalities and on occasion was introduced as "Mr. Alliance." During this period, he served on many municipal and state committees, always contributing a positive and level-headed influence. He shrugged off suggestions of attempting to seek a higher public office because he was contemptuous of politics. Confusing, Eh?

During this period, the man found time to raise five children (with the help of his wife, of course) and had an enviable family life. He was and is regarded as a regular fellow. He retired in 1972 almost completely severing connections with public life, except once when a later Council honored him by appointing him to finish out the term of one of its members, who had died in office. He often said that retirement was tough – trying to play as much golf as he got credit for playing while in office.

The urge to write came over him in these later years. It was probably a throw-back to several journalistic flareups and a stint at reporting for *The Lincoln State Journal* while still in college. This collection contains the contents of two booklets on local historical incidents, some outdoor magazine stories, a bit of comedy, and one as he dubbed it, "a tear jerker."

II

The following story, THE BIG RACE, was submitted to The Writing and Storytelling Festival for Older Nebraskans sponsored by the English Department of University of Nebraska in 1985. It was included and published later in Volume V of that Festival. Perhaps that experience ignited the spark which resulted in assembling this collection into a book.

The Big Race

The boy had just entered the seventh grade and had a lofty conception of his physical prowess. It was with critical eye and jealous heart that he watched the high school cross country team practice. *He was as good as those fellows* – so he started practice running.

Although his workouts were always by him alone, they did not go unnoticed. The high school track coach intercepted him one day and they visited. The boy ventured that he could outrun several of those older boys and would like to try it. The coach was amused, and in his own mind, dubbed the boy as "one cocky kid."

"Well," he said, "We can't run you on the team, but I don't know of any conference rule that would prevent you from running unattached."

The boy would like that very much and the coach proceeded to fill him in on the time and place of the next meet. It was to be held on the municipal golf course. Our boy mustered the nerve to practice run a couple of times with the team and found those fellows were not so slow after all. This observation was not shared with anyone – he still figured he could beat them.

Race day conditions were ideal. Our boy was in awe of the assemblage of various colored uniforms and felt somewhat conspicuous in his Boy Scout shorts and tennis shoes, but nobody could have guessed his inner thoughts – they were so completely masqueraded by his air of confidence.

"Ouch! What was that?" A sharp pain had shot up the boy's side, but was gone immediately. That was good because at the crack of the starter's gun, eighty-odd athletes charged forward, vying for positions. The course was marked with blue flags and measured a little more than two and one-half miles. Footing was good and the boy was running easily.

"Ouch!" There it was again – that pain. This time it was sharper and didn't go away as it had before. He had run just a mile. Another half mile went by. He was now in the middle of the grouping, which now was beginning to string out from the clustered bunching that had started. Another half mile and he couldn't keep up. Soon he was in last place. The leaders were now out of his sight as they turned into the home stretch. Now he would have quit, but to him, the name of the game was fight and to finish. Anyhow, there was no place to hide.

At this point, the sharp turn into the home stretch brought the runners close to a fairway on the back nine of the golf course, which was open for play to the golfers. A foursome had paused to watch the runners make that turn. The boy was in last place. He hurt. His knees were wobbly and he was one sick boy.

"They went that way!" shouted one golfer in the group, causing much laughter from the others.

What an ignoble way to finish? But that sarcastic remark kept the boy going until he was perhaps 200 yards from the finish. His running was now a walk. The coach came to meet him. He saw that he had a sick boy on his hands.

That ended the boy's running for that fall, but the coach said "The young man had plenty of guts!" Guess that's good enough for anybody in his first year of Junior High.

* * * * *

The foregoing story is more-or-less true. The writer was a member of that foursome and laughed with the others. On sober reflection, he realized that it was a cruel barb. It is my sincere hope that the young fellow healed quickly.

III

THE EMPTY PEN is probably the writer's favorite story. It was accepted for and published in the April, 1985 issue of NEBRASKAland, the outdoor mazagine published by the Nebraska Game and Parks Commission.

The Empty Pen

What was that?

I rolled over and pulled the covers higher over my shoulders and tried again to enter that unconscious state of sleep. There it was again! Or, had there really been a first time? But I was sure I had heard a bark. I slipped out of bed and went to the bathroom window as I had done many times before when something had aroused the big lab.

There was nothing in the moonlit yard below to suggest reason for the protective, warning bark. A gentle breeze caused the tree limbs to cast weird, shapeless shadows to dance crazily across the pen, but there was no evidence of an inmate and the gate was ajar just as it was left after the last trip the dog had made with me — to

Mame

the veterinarian. I returned to bed and in a fitful, half-conscious state reviewed most of the past fourteen years with that dog.

First, there was that sunny, cold day in January, 1968. My wife, some months before, had laid down the law—no more dogs! Sir, an extremely talented black labrador, but with a negative reputation in the neighborhood for intimidating pet cats, dogs, and for dirtying bluegrass lawns, was gone after an interesting career of more than twelve years with the Laing family. This day, after reading a certain want ad about the availability of the remaining three lab puppies from a litter of eight (of course they were all females), I magnanimously suggested a Sunday dinner in a city some sixty miles away. There was immediate acceptance. Later, as we finished a very nice meal, I stepped to a phone booth and called the number in the ad.

"What was that all about?" queried the wife upon my return to the table.

"Just a call for an address and to confirm what may well turn out to be a big contribution in our lives," I replied. Then the real purpose of my generosity and thoughtfulness came out. It was received quietly.

"Just look at that!" I said, pointing to a corner house bearing the address I had received.

A large, black mama labrador was nervously patroling the rollicking antics of three roly-poly puppies, which had been released from a nearby dog pen. The scene was being supervised, more or less, by a man, who now picked up the very pup I was watching, cuddled it to his chest and was rewarded with affectionate nuzzling just under his jaw at neck level. I was completely taken by the scene.

Mrs. Laing voiced no objection to my getting out of the car and talking to the man. I believe she actually had softened as she saw the innocent cavorting of those puppies. At least the bars of her ultimatum were now lowered. After a few minutes conversation and the passing of a check to the man, I took the cuddly pup from him, and while the mother dog paced nervously around her two remaining offspring, got into the car with my new charge and responsibility.

"Isn't she a dandy?" I ventured.

"Listen now, you'll have to have her fixed. I'll not put up with another litter and she can't be in the house! I've mopped up my last puddle!"

Well so far so good. I had expected even more conditions. I put the pup on the seat between us and started for home. At first the new addition was nervous but we hadn't gone far before the strain of the afternoon's events so weighed upon our little friend that she nestled down, not close to her new master, but crowded against the lap of mother Laing with her muzzle resting, with trust and affection across her thigh. I felt the battle was won. I smiled and as her hand softly caressed that warm bundle of fur, our eyes met and my smile was rewarded with a smile. Ah! a great helpmate.

"You like to name her?" I asked. "You have a great touch in name choices." She had named Sir when he was just a puppy and it had proved a winner. "Think it over."

"I have it now," she said, "how about Mame?"

So Mame it was. Somehow the suggestion of the Broadway stage and the popular leading lady, brought out smiles and caused people upon hearing it to take a second look at a dog bearing such a moniker. Mame, the dog, it turned out, was just ham enough to lap up the added attention. A procession of events and experiences with Mame tumbled without pattern through the filmy panorama of my dreaming.

The door dog never had the benefit of formal training or obedience school. Instinct more than made up for that, to me at least. She was equally accommodating at retrieving—whether it was for a block of wood in a small pond to the delight of the grandchildren, when they would visit; or, of more sterner stuff, like locating a crippled mallard for me in some dense rushes.

Understanding and affection? That dog had the highest degree of canine charisma. Her initial approach to and acceptance of a new acquaintance, whether canine or humane, was one of friendly tolerance. Then, as if not to overdo the contact, she would become independent and go her way unless there seemed some need to remain with the new company.

Many times in a duck and goose blind with me, she would curl up at my feet resigned to match my patience. I found myself watching her instead of the sky for birds. The whir of wing clipping of a flock would cause her head to be raised to attention. Usually the target would be out of range, but her senses were so strong and accurate, that many times a shot would be my reward.

In the lull between chances (and in hunting there were plenty of lulls) her eyes would close in complete relaxation. Then, nothing would arouse her to attention like my rattling a sack or paper for a lunch or just nibbling. She was unmindful of the metalic click of a cap being unscrewed on a thermos (she didn't care for coffee anyhow) but the rustling of paper usually meant goodies. She would waken, regard me expectantly and if nothing was offered or tossed to her, begin a slow creep along and over my legs from her end of the pit until her patience and drooling were rewarded with a cookie, a bit of sandwich, and she particularly liked to share a can of sardines. I'll miss that dog and her sophisticated tastes.

9

"Good Girl"

Yes, and she knew to whom she belonged. I recall a pheasant hunt in which seven men were trampling out the field with a couple of guards at its end. By the time we reached the end of the field, Mame had retrieved eight birds. All were killed by my companions, but she delivered every bird to me. I was loaded down and hadn't fired a shot. Little sympathy I received from such pals. Their comments were more like, "hope that isn't a game warden over on that county road. Ol' Laing might have some explaining to do. After all, it is his dog."

She was equally good in the water as in the field. I've had her break ice on Curry Lake just to retrieve some of those big, orange-legged, northern mallards. Once in the North Platte River, I thought I had lost her for sure. My host and I dropped three geese out of a flock. I picked one up as it floated dead past the tip of the tow head while Mame was bringing in a second dead goose. She dropped the bird at my feet and turned to locate the third goose, which was crippled and had made its way across the icy channel.

The intense cold of the night before had formed a sheet of ice out from the river bank probably thirty feet wide and extending down the river as far as eye could see. Just before the goose disappeared from sight into the void between the water and the ice, due to the heaving and expansion of the latter, it flipped a wing. That was all the dog needed. She had marked her goal and was gone. Upon reaching the point where we had last seen the bird, without any hesitation whatever, she disappeared under the ice.

Time passed. I became frantic. Worse, I was helpless. I wondered how far down the river she might be swept? Could she get hung up on tree branches or roots? Had I lost my dog? After what must have been three or four minutes but which seemed like an age, she reappeared towing the injured goose gingerly by the wing joint. There was too much life left in the bird to risk loosening her bite.

Every so often coming across that channel of slush ice, the big goose would take new life and really beat the dog with its good wing. Mame took those vicious pelts across her head as a matter of course. She was not releasing that wing joint and losing the bird. Not until she reached the bank of our island and had tugged the exhausted goose onto solid ground, did she release her hold and lay down completely spent.

Risking her life. Spending all that time in an icy river. Performing so courageously. For what? Approval from her master? Well she got that. A pat on the head and the *Good Girl* assurance, repeated over and over, seemed all she expected and received.

I never laughed at or made light of that river incident, but Mame's first pheasant was another matter. We were sort of road hunting while looking for a likely weed patch. The dog, riding in the back seat, just had been admonished for having her cold wet nose on the back of my neck, when I saw a nice rooster run across an open area and into a patch of grass and weeds. Mame saw him too and almost went berserk. I stopped the car and we took in after the bird. Getting across the borrow pit and through the fence was no problem for the dog, but by the time I could shoot legally, she was pell-mell into that weed patch. The bird exploded out and over a field of green winter wheat with Mame in hot pursuit. I dropped Mr. pheasant with a first shot, but he had plenty of life left in him. He was flopping crazily and to the dog that meant he was getting away. She hit him with a vengeance. There was a cloud of feathers and for her reckless abandon Mame received a slash across the nose from the bird's spur. Again, that called for more decisive action—clamp down on that wriggling body and prevent any recurrence of such impudence. When she brought the bird to me, she had taken him by the back and those strong young jaws had crushed most of the bone structure of the pheasant.

If I had any complaint on Mame's retrieving, it was on pheasants, especially if they had any life left in them. If the bird was dead and still, she didn't treat it the same way, but she sure wasn't taking any chances of getting another slash across the nose. With ducks it was different. There was never a tooth mark on the breast or body of a duck that she retrieved.

Occasionally she was called upon to retrieve a grouse. That was almost ludicrous. Invariably she would pick up the bird and then literally spit it out. I had not seen a dog spit before, but that seems the best description of her attempts to rid her mouth of those soft dry feathers. Afterwards, she would nudge the bird over, pick it up from the back rather than the breast and retrieve.

Mame wasn't capable of having any common, ordinary experience. Or is that the pride of a loving master showing? Well anyhow, she was a beautiful, big black labrador—well kept and with good eyes, mouth and a classic head. What could possibly torment such a perfect creature? Well the veterinarian had a name for it; and, I guess dysplasia is not uncommon in this breed. With Mame, through the past few years, it had worsened progressively until her almost every movement was a painful effort. As a last resort, I took her to the lake and she seemed to enjoy fetching the block of wood, but it was apparent that she could not cope with that river current. Then I took her grouse hunting, knowing full well what the outcome of that would be—she just couldn't make it and keep up. Our next trip was to the veterinarian. Old Mame nuzzled his hand as he administered the shot—the same hand that had pricked her with a needle before—for distemper when she was a puppy and later periodically for her rabies shot. Then she just laid her head down and passed into dog heaven without even a whimper.

* * * * *

When I came down to breakfast the next morning, I stood at the window with a cup of coffee in hand and gazed thoughtfully and sadly at that pen. It had been a daily routine—to first feed Mame and see that she had a clean pan of water. I wondered what now would take the place of that daily chore. The pen was empty.

IV

What happened – mixing a poem with the prose of storytelling? Well, the writer just couldn't help it. In going through some of his deceased mother's things, he found WHEN HUNTING DAYS ARE O'ER. Faded yellow and brittle with more than sixty years of storage in a dresser drawer, it sort of confirmed that "R. W." had always been sort of sentimental and perhaps a bit corny.

When Hunting Days Are O'er

When September's gold had faded, and
    we've harked to the heron's cry,
When the youngest duckling had feathered,
    and long since learned to fly,
We would hunt. And how we'd enjoy it —
    that building of friendship true.
Bill and I, with dog and gun, out under
    the heaven's blue.

And October's glory, it has gone too,
    now a memory of the past.
Of days afield with dog and gun, and
    grouse that were flushing fast.
It was great sport, to try our skill,
    gunning for such game,
With praise for hits and for a miss —
    a friendly jest or blame.

Then November's fascination, when her
    sharp, chill winds came forth
Driving myriads of hardy waterfowl
    down from the ice-clad north;
We matched our skill with duck and goose,
    yes for them all we gamed.
'Tis the greatest sport in all the world!
    Both Bill and I acclaimed.

Now Bill and I are old and stiff, our
    hunting days are passed.
Thank God we have our memories still to
    make those good times last.
For each in the joy of reminiscing those
    visions of days gone by
Shall recall each scene as we lived it —
    dog, gun, Bill and I.

V

Included in SHORT STORY SMORGASBORD
are two writings that have been published
previously as pamphlets (LEGEND AND
MEMORY 1979 and PHASE 11 of L & M
1980). Duplication, of course, but we trust the
pamphlet owners will concur – that they also
belong in the SMORGASBORD.

Legend and Memory

INTRODUCTION

Footsteps coming upstairs creaked to signal that someone was coming, probably to check on the small five-year-old boy who was peeking under the drawn window shade watching "the action" below on Box Butte Avenue one night in 1911 – for the town had been voted "dry" effective midnight. There were definitely spectacles to be witnessed from such a vantage point upstairs over the Central Cafe in the 200 block of Box Butte Avenue, which block also boasted or apologized, depending upon personal viewpoints, for five of the seven saloons in Alliance, Nebraska at that time.

The boy, that was me, dived back into bed and was the picture of innocence and nocturnal unconsciousness as Mother, free for the moment of her cashier's duties at the front of the restaurant counter of the cafe owned and operated by Mr. Laing, carefully opened the door, tiptoed in, lovingly tucked a cover higher on the boy's shoulder, checked with a quick glance that the windowshade was pulled down to a maximum to shield the young fellow from the iniquities of the street and then quietly left the room and returned to her duties downstairs. Cy, "C.A." or Sarpy, as Dad was affectionately known, disliked anyone but family manning that cash register very long at a time.

Needless to say, the boy was back at the window as soon as the footsteps faded. Below was taking place a scene of boisterous hilarity – shouting, raucous laughing and "carryings on" by adult men (women were, of course, notably absent). That experience was not to be equaled some nine years later, in 1920, when the Volstead Act and prohibition went into effect throughout the nation. At least, not as "the boy" remembered.

Tiring of the revelries' sameness, he was just about to give up and return to bed, when a number of shots rang out. There was a significant silence following, broken by boisterous yells and an occasional shot as the commotion, which probably began west of the Burlington tracks on Third Street and outside the city limits, drew nearer and finally unfolded "live" in the dusty main street below him. Verily, this was exciting! Fifteen or twenty cowboys, laughing

19

and yelling, tied their mounts to the hitching rail along the wooden planked sidewalk in front of Simon Spry's saloon and with much backslapping and swaggering entered the place for a last night of revelry. At the breakfast counter next morning someone said that it was a bunch of the cowhands from Charlie Tiernan's outfit. There was no more gunfire, but there was an occasional outburst of yelling, often profane, and as midnight came and passed, quiet prevailed and the young fellow above mentioned "gave up" and returned to bed and dreamland.

* * * * *

Alliance, Nebraska 1896. Taken from Burlington Smoke Stack looking north.

Sixty-seven years later this "then-a-boy-of-five" recalling that experience, reasoned that he had witnessed, or been close to, a number of interesting events in Alliance history and had really been a part of much of its panorama of change and while many events and effects are conceptions as seen through his eyes, perhaps they should be set down in some sort of narrative, and it is with that purpose in mind that he has assembled the following story.

I. Early Alliance

First, let it be clearly understood that this is not intended as an all inclusive history of the City of Alliance. So many things included in the very factual HISTORY OF BOX BUTTE COUNTY, written and released in 1939, by Anna M. Phillips and Vilma D. Ball, was also Alliance history, that there may be overlapping but not plagiarism. This is a story, legendary or of record prior to 1907 (or 1911 or whatever date recall is impressed upon "a young fellow's memory") of events he was intimately close to or had actually observed or witnessed. In 1938, as City Clerk and City Manager Hoper's assistant, we presented the City's Annual Report for 1937 in form and content appropriate for that year's Golden Jubilee. This contained a section on Alliance history from data furnished by Mrs. Reuben Knight and Fred Harris. Certainly some credit must be given these people, especially Mrs. Knight who also made contributions to the Phillips-Ball book.

Alliance was incorporated by the County Commissioners as a village in 1888, one year after the Lincoln Land Company, made up largely of railroad officials, purchased 600 acres of land at a public auction held in Nonpareil. The purchased land was believed to be the site which would be the junction of the railroad's division lines. Its construction at the time had extended as far west as Anselmo, Nebraska. Probably the second entry on most abstracts of title to property in that original part of the city incorporated from Section 36, T-25-N, R-48-W of the 6th P.M., Box Butte County, Nebraska, shows The Lincoln Land Company as the grantee.

Legend has it that a Mr. J. N. Paul, a civil engineer with an advance construction crew, suggested the name of Alliance. Paul was also identified with St. Paul, Nebraska, which causes speculation if there was any family connection between him and R. T. (Bob) Paul who worked on several paving and improvement districts in Alliance as a consultant with offices in St. Paul, Nebraska, from 1948 to the 1970's.

The story of the county seat being moved from Nonpareil to Hemingford and then to Alliance with transportation of the Hemingford courthouse to Alliance by railroad flat cars is well known.

The town's growth mushroomed into a rough western town in its early years. Several bad fires in 1892 and 1893 pushed the village board into its first bonded indebtedness for a water system. The frequency of fires to frame buildings also led to the adoption of

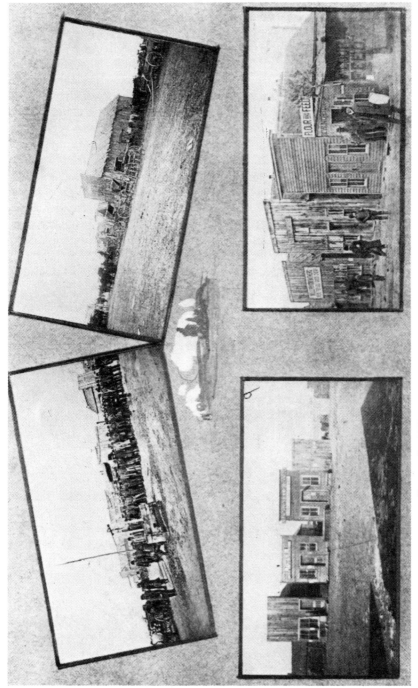

Scenes in Alliance, 1888. Note Town well in upper left.

an ordinance prohibiting construction in a fire zone of materials other than fireproof material. This justified a brick yard. Many of the older downtown buildings and some dwellings to this day show the attempt at compliance by using this inferior local brick. When constructed the water system dictated the removal of the town well and pump from the middle of Box Butte Avenue but the public horse watering tank in front of the City Hall across Third Street from Schafer's garage remained and, while discontinued a few years later, it's complete removal and separation from the water main was not completed until the old city hall was razed in 1943 to make way for the U.S.O. building erected during the Airbase days.

One of the greatest moves made by the early City Fathers was the inclusion of an option-to-purchase in the franchise given private interests to operate a "light plant." After four years of such utility operation, an appraisal of $78,000.00 was made of the property and the village purchased the power plant for $55,000.00 March 18, 1911. A bond issue was required in the amount of $20,000.00 at a 4½% interest rate. The following rate schedule was adopted and remained until 1915:

Residences

First	30	Kwh	15¢ per Kwh
Next	70	Kwh	11¢ per Kwh
Above	100	Kwh	Same as Stores

Store Rates

First	100	Kwh	12¢ per Kwh
Next	200	Kwh	8¢ per Kwh
Next	200	Kwh	6¢ per Kwh
Above	500	Kwh	8¢ on total amount used

Power

First	100	Kwh	12¢ per Kwh
Next	100	Kwh	7¢ per Kwh
Next	100	Kwh	5¢ per Kwh
Next	200	Kwh	4¢ per Kwh
Next	500	Kwh	3¢ per Kwh
Above	1000	Kwh	4½¢ for full amount used

Electric Range

First	50	Kwh	7¢ per Kwh
Above	50	Kwh	5¢ per Kwh

Minimum bill on each service, $1.50 per month
10% discount allowed if bills were paid in 10 days

In the interesting history of the Village's entry into and operation of such a proprietary, as distinguished from governmental function, was the adoption of meter deposits to safeguard electric accounts in 1917 and 1918 on account of the transient population brought about by the potash boom in Hoffland, Antioch and Lakeside, all within 25 miles of the town, the numerous traveling men and the hard-to-pin-down railroad man. The latter, particularly in the train service, was hard to establish residence for at assessment time for tax purposes. It was soon to follow, with the power plant's operation one of the salient factors, that the form of local government was changed to the Council Manager form of government.

The Town had a Mayor-Council form of government until 1921 although an attempt to adopt something similar to a manager plan was made in 1919. Mayor A. D. Rodgers, realizing that he was a better grocerman than a power plant head, appointed a man by the name of Cassius C. Smith as "City Manager and Superintendent of Utilities." His authority to make such an appointment was in an ordinance adopted for the purpose but without the enabling state law to make it legal. Mr. Smith had his troubles. The fact that little foresight had been given to the coal mine and railroad sympathy strikes and that the town ran completely out of coal for both domestic and power plant use was hardly his fault but it certainly contributed to his demise and short tenure.

Subsequently, the Council-Manager Plan act was passed by the then two-house state legislature and after being petitioned properly and voted on favorably in an election, was adopted and went into effect in 1921. By a vote of 699 to 53 Alliance became the first city in the state to adopt the plan, a distinction it bore until 1948 when a rash of adoptions took place over the next few years in some nine Nebraska cities. The Alliance story became a state-wide one that, in each election on adopting the plan, was held up as a record of clean and efficient government which, with a business-like method of operation made possible so many of the City's material assets — parks, paving, drainage, sewage system, library, cemetery, airport and many others. In 58 years Alliance has had only seven managers. (One of these was for only eight months.) Such tenure reflects the local acceptance of the plan, and the low interest rates Alliance bonds have always attracted reflect the high regard it has enjoyed with municipal bond houses and investors.

II. The Railroad Town

Alliance has always been a "railroad town." Although many council members have been railroaders, only five of the forty-one mayors since 1888 have been so identified. That the Mayor was elected, by the people directly prior to 1921 and by the five-man council since, seems to have little importance. The mayorship distinction has usually gone to a professional or business man. However, the influence of "the largest payroll in town," with the railroad shops and repair facilities for three divisions (Lincoln-Billings, Sterling and Casper) as well as the train service was not without considerable clout. There is no denying there were social cliques, especially in the early part of the century, when some disgruntled person might be heard to refer occasionally to "the railroad aristocracy." The trend for railroad people (the employees) to organize and socialize by union classification—Brotherhood of Locomotive Engineers (B of L. E.), Brotherhood of Locomotive Firemen and Engineers (B of L. F. & E.), Order of Railway Conductors (O. R. C.) et cetera, with perhaps a Ladies Auxiliary to each, spread rather thin any unified dominance that might have played havoc to the peaceful, political balance in the city.

Burlington passenger depot with baggage trucks in foreground.

In the first fifty years in the life of the Town, the railroad had replaced the antiquated wagon freighter and became the only mode of transportation of heavy goods and livestock to and from distant markets. However, as trail roads became surfaced highways, first gravel and then by the higher class bituminous and concrete, the automotive truck came into competitive importance. Alliance had always had extensive stockyard pens adjacent the railroad yards when train loads of cattle, hogs and sheep from Wyoming, Montana, South Dakota and western Nebraska, could he held over, if desired, to feed and water, enroute to the fattening cornfields and feedlots in Iowa, Illinois and eastern Nebraska and eventually to the large packing plants in Omaha or Chicago. This was a profitable haul for the railroad and it was occasionally observed by a critic that "a trainload of cattle received more attention and arrived in Chicago faster than a paying fare on a passenger train." This was not always true, of course, for except for the mainline passenger service (Chicago-Denver) for which the Mainliner and the Zepher were developed, service was remarkable when travel comfort and schedule convenience were considered.

At any rate, with development of the truck and the use of the large stock-trailers, the livestock business for the railroad dwindled

Alliance Livestock Commission Company led in sales over Nebraska for many years.

27

to practically zero. Hardly a critter was moved by rail from the Alliance Livestock Commission Company in later years. Originally the Commission Company had been located on railroad property, near the stockyards and sidetracks because its operation and the railroad's was really a "love affair." Not so with the increasing use of the large semi-trailer's convenience and economies. These newcomers did not require a costly crew, maintenance of a roadbed and track and there was much less regulation by commissions and timetable schedules.

The railroad for economic reasons became more and more interested in the long haul than in providing good local service although there was a rather feeble effort made to fill the local-haul-gap when it went to the truck in its own operation between Scottsbluff and Alliance. The less-than-carload-lot (LCL) policy meant inconvenience to dozens of smaller towns that in the past had received good local service. No wonder that truck service became more popular. With having cut all passenger service and having to match the trucks and semi-trailers, rail service now has been tailored to the hauling of the heavy stuff—lumber, oil, cement, gravel, grain—at least seasonally, "piggy-backing" automobiles and even semi-trailers, and of course, the present stepped-up and life-saving bonanza of the coal haul from the low sulphur-content coal fields of Wyoming and beyond to satisfy environmental pollution requirements of the industrial east.

The last regularly scheduled passenger train through Alliance was discontinued August 25, 1969. There is now no passenger service on any of the divisions out of Alliance . . . What a contrast with the eight arrivals and departures of some twenty years before. Compliance with costly union agreements, the public's expectancy for high class of service and loss of revenue to the automobile and airplane could not be justified. This writer also must add this observation because, though far from being a railroad professional, he has always been interested, and has noted that there were always dozens of passenger boardings right up to the last train. Analyzing these boarders indicated that by far the majority of them were "free riders." There were just too many passengers that, as employees, members of the clergy, plus others who came in varied and elastic categories such as certain political, military, educational figures and citizens of prominance that for one reason or other traveled on a pass or "rated" a discounted fare.

Two almost forgotten fields in the old passenger train days were the Pullman and Dining Car services. Dining service offered excellent cuisine when compared with the traveler's old banana, apple and sandwich, brown-bag lunch; and the Pullman car offered a crisp and clean upper or lower berth with complete toilet and restroom facilities.

It was most luxurious and restful to the departing passenger who could board in Alliance about 11:00 p.m. and arrive with a good night's sleep in Lincoln or Omaha at 6:00 or 8:00 a.m., conduct a day's business and be back home via a "sleeper" at 7:00 a.m. the following morning.

Except for the white dining steward and the Pullman conductor, these crews were predominantly colored. Alliance was a "change point" for crews of both services. This fact contributed numerically to the local black population of the twenties and early thirties until the dining headquarters was established at Lincoln and the Pullman porter made a run that began and terminated in Kansas City, Missouri. At one time there were 800 blacks in Alliance's total population of 6,669 people. Even after the general exodus of blacks to stay with their jobs, a number of families continued to live in Alliance and such names as the Selbys, Woodleys, Sheltons, Taylors, Slaughters, Chandler, Nickens and English are within memory's reach. At the height of this unusual racial mix, there was a colored saloon and two restaurants – the All Nations Cafe and 101 Sweetwater. Some, like the Batt, Shelton and Nelson families, even took up farming.

III. Organizations

The TPA, as the Travelers' Protective Association was known, was a fraternal organization of traveling men. It provided a life insurance plan with certain sick and disability benefits on an assessment premium basis for which the cost varied with the number of members enrolled. Prior to World War I it was the one organization that could and did supply supplemental official police, firemen and sheriff deputies and such public services as could be expected of an auxiliary organization in times of emergency, such as the influenza epidemic of 1918, handling ticket sales, crowd control and traffic at circuses, carnivals, and Stockmen's annual rodeo programs. The TPA, a generation later, its ranks depleted in numbers, was more or less replaced following World War I by the American Legion, then made up of younger and more energetic men. These Veterans furnished the volunteer services for the next 15 or 20 years and as the fires and energy of this admirable and public spirited service organization also waned, its function in this respect was slowly supplanted by members of the Chamber of Commerce and the Jaycees.

Back in the Twenties there was no Chamber of Commerce by that name. Businessmen felt there should be an organization to promote Alliance beyond what could be expected of elected city officials. About this time the Potash Highway, as present State Highway No. 2 was then known as least locally, was eligible for some improvement but its importance had to be promoted. The Commercial Club was organized and because no local leader had the time to promote and run this new organization, a man by the name of Fisher was hired to do so. Fisher was a pusher, full of energy and new ideas and lasted for several years with a good showing of results especially beneficial to Alliance retailers and highway improvement. The organization and legal incorporation of the Alliance Chamber of Commerce subsequently followed, with a paid Secretary-Manager and a membership in the U.S. Chamber of Commerce.

Alliance's early day burial grounds was located a couple of blocks south of the Potash Avenue underpass in South Alliance. It served the purpose for those times but as people really established their homes-to-be in Alliance, the Alliance Cemetery Association was formed and a more appropriate location sought. In 1896 an acreage was purchased in the cemetery's present location, and the interred bodies were removed from the old "boot hill" type graveyard. Most of those burials had been for the bodies of early day adventurers, cow hands, drifters and individuals without too much in the way of family or connections to provide identification. These bodies in turn were interred in a triangular unplatted area in what is now the heart of the cemetery. Many of those graves are unmarked.

The Association did a little better job of cemetery administration but in 1915 prevailed upon the City to take over the cemetery. The entire records of lot ownership and burials were found on a back shelf of Si Miller's Shoe Store. Si was secretary of the Association. By about 1921, record keeping, surveys and beautification of the grounds were greatly improved as the City Administration realized what it had been handed.

Bob Eaton's funeral. Death from scalding in railroad wreck 1897.

IV. Business and Change

Business in Alliance always has been good compared with many other communities – so much so that business policies may have been a bit conservative. The railroad payroll was a regular thing and kept money available to be spent at a more or less uniform level. Business health was more or less on a cash basis as contrasted to the neighboring Valley of the Nile along the Platte River with its irrigation and beet and bean crops which dictated the extension of credit by merchants and professions alike until late fall when the season's beet checks became available.

One incident, illustrating this "cash" rather than "credit" concept locally, involved the loss of Chadron State College, or at least a better chance at its being located in Alliance. Monte S. Hargraves, Secretary of the Alliance Building and Loan Association, was a very influential personality. He was pretty much completely in command of the only institution in town dealing in rentals, home financing and urban real estate. Somehow when a Site Board checked on Alliance for a location to establish a State Normal School, Monte was about the only local individual contacted. He was very cool and even curt to the Site Board which was looking for a quarter section of land close to town for the school's campus. Almost begrudgingly Monte conducted the Board to look at the quarter section northeast of town on part of which Lampert Lumber Company is now located. This was during a driving snowstorm when six or eight inches of snow was already on the ground. It would have made a beautiful site for the campus and its expansion. There was no invitation issued to return later and take a second look under better conditions. In fact, Monte expressed his own opinion as to "whether Alliance wanted a school which would bring in a bunch of 'Young Spenders' without means of their own and of dubious credit standing at an age of irresponsibility." Certainly Alliance retailers had no say in the impression given and the Site Board went on to Chadron, which had already expressed an interest in the school which was ultimately located in that city.

Hargraves was the same "sage" that predicted Box Butte Avenue would be the street on which business would expand – that even "automobile row" would in time extend north of Sixth Street. Giving him the benefit of the doubt, that prediction was probably based on the new Lowery-Henry garage built at that time and his thinking it was the beginning of a trend.

32

Retailing progress in Alliance was persistent and business developed from the wood-coal-and-feed store in step with the nation through the coal oil (kerosene), coal and the stoker, fuel oil, manufactured bottle gas to natural gas and as this is written, with a threatened nationwide energy shortage, there are ingenious innovations being tried dealing with effective ways of capturing solar energy for heating and industrial uses.

Clothing and fabric merchandising outlets developed and flourished. Particularly in the teens and the twenties, such names as Bogue, Mollering, W. R. Harper and Golden Rule (Barnett) department stores; The Famous (Frankle), E. G. Laing Clothing, Roy Beckwith and Pete Manewal's men's stores. Later it was Rhoads, Thelma's and the Fashion Shop (Isaacson) offering exclusively, ladies ready to wear. Millinery flourished in the early days. Of course the writer wasn't much interested in ladies fine feathered hats at that time, but does recall a quaint old lady by the name of Fox that engaged in that business on West Third Street. Emma Mallette, a Miss O'Connell and a partnership of Cora Pauley and Carman Gore made and sold hats much later but the fashion seemed to go out of style about the time World War II ended.

Changes in materials over the years – cotton and wool garments replaced, supplanted and modified by polyester, orlon, et cetera, were not without effect on the mortality of some stores but affected mostly some of the services incident to the care of clothes.

Who now remembers that the town's laundry was once run by a Chinaman? The writer remembers him well enough and was fascinated no end by his queue (pigtail, we called it). However, individually he kept to himself and was somewhat of a mystery and my knowledge of the laundry business then was pretty much limited to Monday workouts manually turning the washing machine on the back porch (in the kitchen, of course, in the winter) for Mother. Today the popularity of the drip-dry fabrics and the use of automatic washers and dryers and the coin operated laundries have made the Alliance Steam Laundry, Alliance Hotel Laundry, Steggs, Mullender and others, including the erstwhile washerwoman of which there were dozens, only memories.

A similar transition occurred in the drycleaning business. Twenty years ago there were five quite modern and thriving plants – Keep-U-Neat (Bradbury then Tatum), Brennans (Martin and Joe), Modern (Buck), Bet-R-Way Cleaners (Copple) and the Alliance Sta-Nu (Ushio). Only the latter is in business today. None of these plants failed, but as the permanent press fabrics developed, the trade just became too much of a "rat race" to be inviting to new managements.

33

Any account of the grocery business would have to cover the demise of the Independent and neighborhood store groceries before the merchandising blitz of the Super Market. Where up to the twenties the home-owned grocery, usually with a butcher shop or meat market, was the rule. Some were "cash and carry"; others extended credit and some developed various modes of delivery – first the horse-drawn runabout or drays; later it was the flat bed truck or pickup piloted by some teenager what broke the eggs, mashed the bread, lost small items and spilled from poorly capped containers. Storekeepers were legion, but the names of Buechsenstein, Duncan & Son, Mallery, Essay, Stalos, Rodgers, Lee Moore, Corner Grocery (Davee), Missouri Market (Moore), Central Market (Bills), and Grandview which is just phasing out its existence at this writing.

Dwight Zediker's Livery Service. Site of Eagles Building.

An interesting sidelight is the history of Fourth Street Market. Harness Hirst had a grocery store in the Masonic Temple building at Third and Laramie. In the very early twenties, he took on a World War I veteran, Virgil L. Lehr, a man of boundless energy and drive, as a partner. The store had been operated as Hirst's, next it became Hirst and Lehr and moved across the alley from Newberry Hardware Store and became Lehr and Hirst's Fourth Street Market, then finally just Lehr's. This is not to imply that Hirst was "frozen out" of the business without proper compensation. The difference in ages, the vigorous makeup of the younger man, and the different characteristics of the two men just naturally dictated the end of their association with Lehr emerging as the city's leading Independent in the very competitive and often bitter struggle for survival against the Super Markets.

Two Super Markets started up in Alliance about the same time — Piggly Wiggley and Skaggs. Local merchants were quite alarmed by these and the stories from other communities that followed, predicting the fate of all Independents which could not compete with the dreaded chain store. The prognosis proved to be correct. One by one the local Independents succumbed to superior merchandising techniques, expert trained management and, of course, low, competitive price cutting.

One of the last to go, and he did it with dignity by selling out and leaving to eventually head his father-in-law's bank in southeastern Nebraska, was Virg Lehr. Lehr's energy and bulldog tactics in those crazy twenties, kept the local "chains" on their toes. Both Piggley Wiggley and Skaggs felt the barb of his relentless competitive drive and eventually were phased into the Safeway Store located at Third and Laramie. Subsequently, the number of "supers" increased — Safeway, Jack and Jill, Deveny's, and just recently the U-Save store.

Lehr's constant promotions and price-meeting phobia made his name highly respected in the Safeway Denver Division Office. Nothing stumped the man. A rumor that the chain was selling something for 2¢ a pound under his price caused an immediate check and an adjusted price. He was always paying a little more for eggs if "taken out in trade" and country butter had to smell pretty bad for him to refuse to take it off the farm wife's hands but then there was always the "not the next time unless it is sweet" admonishment.

The sugar market presented an incongruous situation for Alliance grocers. Bayard's sugar factory was only forty miles away, and the beet was grown in that area. However, the price of sugar, set in Chicago, was "pegged," through some complicated freight rate zoning, so that the Alliance consignee benefited. Lehr had a heyday! He had a carlot sugar sale by the 100 pound bag monthly. It was some little time before competition figured out why so many valley farmers were trading at Fourth Street Market in Alliance. Well, for 2¢ a pound savings (and Lehr limited them to five bags per customer) they could and did make the trip for the $10.00 savings. The 48 pound sack of flour was another of his "leaders" but the detail of that trick escapes the writer. Such "come-ons" would not work today as "leaders" as few housewives bake, can fruit, or use those two ingredients to the extent their mothers did in the 1920's.

One thing that did affect the housewife's convenience was the phasing out of the neighborhood store. This came about as a result of price and choice offered by "downtown" competition and the adoption of zoning ordinances by the city. This permitted the continuance of the neighborhood store under a "grandfather" clause at the location at the time but if the commercial activity ceased for a sixty day period or more the property reverted to a strictly residential use with any commercial rebirth prohibited. Filling stations in a residential zone were also affected by this legislation. Many will recall the Eighth Street Market (Milburn), Fifth Street Grocery (Daisy Kelly), Tenth Street Grocery (Kelly and then Stephens), Cheyenne Grocery (Bernard and then Hacker-Davee), Connie Dobson's and others, including Kastner's.

The latter lent an interesting sidelight at city council meetings in the early thirties. Earl D. Mallery, groceryman, was then mayor. The zoning effect on "neighborhoods," coupled with "store hours," immediately caused his "locking horns" with grocerman Leo Kastner, who was himself a feisty individual. This cleavage was contained, however, to a sort of growling and constant watchdogging of each other which did not change after Mallery resigned as mayor, sold the store and became Alliance's third city manager.

V. Restaurants, Hotels and Such

Alliance has never been noted for fancy restaurants. Those places which offered any semblance of dining, as contrasted to "eating," would probably be limited to the cafes in the Alliance and Drake hotels and to Lyle Hare's Alliance Country Club. However, there were many "eating houses," just as there are an abundance of the "fast food" places today. Notably these were the Manhattan Cafe, The Maryland, The Central and the Silver Grill. Restaurant "help," as the employees are usually called, are a type unto themselves. Many are characters but whether prompted by an urge seeking popularity, covering an inferiority complex or just a natural desire to always present a front of rollicking good nature, early-day restaurant help were certainly interesting, particularly the cooks. There was John (Spaghet) Sanderson with the terrible temper that boiled over one night and pursued Louie Karrus, the dishwasher, out the backdoor and down the alley brandishing a long knife with great bodily harm definitely in mind. There was Stub Manure, another of Cy Laing's cooks, and probably the most gifted, that liked to sing. The current popular songs "In the Blue Ridge Mountains of Virginia," "When You Called Me Dearie and I Wore A Great Big Rose" were just a few, but Stub had a profane parody for all of them. That's probably why Mother Laing hated the man and forbade the boy from spending too much time around the kitchen where he often "helped with the silverware." Cy put up with Stub because, like today, good cooks were hard to find.

Such names of owners that come to mind include Jesse Miller, George Milburn, Bill Becker, Dick Becker, "Dad" Noggle, Verlene McCormick, Johnny Sanderson, and Cy Laing. And there were others, some of which definitely fell into the "greasy spoon" category.

One, not in that category, but of historic interest, was Rex Hamburger Shop. Rex Myer's 5¢ "burgers" filled the stomach of many hungry people through a recession and the great depression. That nickel hamburger fried in deep fat right before your eyes was done according to Rex's "secret formula" and was really tasty, and he kept the price down as long as he could. The real test of his respect for his clientele's feelings, and pocketbook, came in the forties and fifties when coffee in most places jumped to 10¢ and 15¢. Rex doggedly held his java to 7¢ a cup, with or without his rather detailed reasoning for the two instead of five cent raise, and he made friends doing so.

The Boarding House was also popular in the early days. It was usually run by a widowed housewife with a lot of pride about making ends meet and catered home-cooked meals, usually to a regular group. Many acquaintances, who were usually office workers and clerks, were regulars at Lena Basye's, at about 508 Cheyenne, who set a fine table of good home-cooked food for many years.

Maypoint, housed in a converted CCC barrack of the thirties, was the community's first supper club as such. The management usually "looked the other way" on spiking from one's own bottle. It offered grilled steaks, shrimp and french fries. The steak was usually a fillet, the size of which might vary from a quarter pound to a thick slab covering an entire platter. As Hans Jaggers said, "Always order a steak with a bone in it." The advice might not always have been 100% correct but it did cut down the odds on being served a slice of loin from a cutter, a canner, or an old bull. Bill Turgeon was the entrepreneur for this operation.

Post War II made a notable contribution to the "supper club" concept. The transient soldier was often used to the drink and eat offerings prevalent in larger and older places. It wasn't long before the fraternal organizations—Elks, Eagles, Legion, VFW and others began using their kitchens at least weekly. Some also catered noon lunches. Without the Two Martini Lunch, the latter pretty much fell from its own weight—most of the patrons had to be back at work by one o'clock.

The hotel picture in Alliance has always been commercially typed as contrasted to resort; the Drake and the Alliance have always been fixtures, but now are being challenged by the motels in competing for the traveling public. The Alliance, after several years inactivity, has been renovated into apartments . . . and then there was one. Chris Abbott offered to build a new hotel, which would have also housed the new Guardian State Bank at the time, if the liquor-by-the-drink question would carry in the 1954 election. That testimony was used freely by proponents for the issue but it nevertheless failed to get the necessary votes to carry at the polls. The Commercial, the Barry House and a number of upstairs rooming houses will be remembered by the cowboy and traveling man. The names of Drake, Newmeyer, Carlile, Reynolds, Manning and Hunter will be associated with the Drake, and Jesse Miller with the Alliance.

In the early days, Alliance had the reputation of being a wide-open town. It was voted dry in 1911 and the Volstead Act, or Prohibition, went into effect in 1920 until repealed effective in 1935. It was extremely unpopular with a large segment of people who defied this "law which curbed their rights" by patronizing bootleggers, making their own home brew, and in general making a farce of all enforcement. Such a situation encouraged nationwide crime. Gangsters engaged in rum-running, operated speakeasies, engaged in prostitution and almost any illegal activity that would "turn a buck." The result was repeal of that Eighteenth Amendment.

That made a problem for local governments, whose officials did not wish to adopt a licensing procedure that would encourage and revert to the old saloon. In Nebraska it was sought to be done by separating beer and liquor by types of licensing for each — off-sale by the package and on-sale by the drink, except in the case of beer. Alliance had to vote three times to get the Class A type privilege (liquor by the drink) and through that period interim bottle clubs flourished, particularly in clubs because the Liquor Commission had a hard and fast definition of a club and the purpose of its formation was one of the big musts. That did pretty well control offering of hard liquor by the drink on a public basis.

Houses of prostitution (whorehouses to the more plain-spoken) did exist and flourish earlier in this rough western town. However, to the writer's knowledge, no saloon enjoyed the convenience of Miss Kitty's Long Branch with the rooms just upstairs. The city fathers, in those early days, were quite aware of the hosues, with such historic madams as Silver Nell Thompson and Rae Weston, but thought of them as a necessary evil and just *hoped they would always remain below Third Street!*

VI. Industry

Newspapers certainly deserve a spot in the panorama of the city's growth. The *Times,* the *Grip* and the *Herald* dispensed local news before the writer's memory. Since, the *Herald* (George and Eddie Burr), the *News* (Ben and Ida Brewster) and the *Times* and *Herald* (first as a semi-weekly with Ben J. Sallows) and later as a semi-weekly then as a "daily" (by Gene Kemper with an affiliation of some sort with the Seaton papers) have all made their contribution in the city's progress.

Manufacturing has had a spotty, though interesting, history. Probably the oldest industry or firm, and of the longest life, was the Newberry Hardware Company, founded by C. A. (Chenia) Newberry soon after he arrived in Alliance in 1888. It started as a tin shop, endured through a disastrous fire, was rebuilt and was added to in various phases to meet the needs of an expanding retail and wholesale hardware business.

A three story retail store, stocking all types of hardware known at the time, was constructed in 1914. Primarily, the manufacturing activity was beamed at the farm-ranch needs in a six-state area. Newberry kept three traveling men covering western Nebraska, North and South Dakota, Wyoming, Montana, and parts of Colorado; and his stock tanks, harness and saddles, windmills and granaries are in existence today, preserved on some ranches that were also "good housekeepers."

The firm was pretty much a family affair after Chenia's death just five months after the failure of the First National Bank which was headed by his son-in-law Frank Abegg. The store was managed in turn by Norman, Chenia's son, and then upon his death, by Bernie Girard, a son-in-law, who throughout the twenties had driven many a dusty and snowy mile selling Newberry-made products. Influenced and guided by Chenia's widow and a trusted old-time employee, George Deitlien, and affected, of course, by the Great Depression, the manufacturing, wholesaling and retail store operations in turn dwindled. The tin shop was discontinued with the retirement of George Dorr, a long-time old-school type foreman; and the saddle and harness making need was dissipated as use of tractors and automobiles increased. The Denver Dry Goods Company fell heir to at least three of Newberry's skilled saddle makers – John Noack, Bob Grove, and Al Yagaditch.

Newberry's Hardware Company—circa 1920, Retail store and two warehouses.

The worth and status of the company's corporate stock became a common speculation of Box Butte Avenue in that period of "tight money" and it was odd, but not altogether strange either, that several of the board members of the ill-fated bank were also substantial Newberry stockholders . . . all were aptly dubbed by Marcus Frankle, owner of the Famous and also a bank director, as Empire Builders.

The store ceased operations as Newberry's in 1968, when it became part of the Ace Hardware chain which finally closed its doors. The only "Newberry" identity now is Bernies, an Ace affiliate owned and ably operated by Chenia's grandson, Bernard Girard, Jr.

Another landmark in Alliance history, with which C. A. Newberry was associated, was the Alliance Creamery Company. It was formed in 1907 with Newberry and W. E. Spencer as co-founders. The latter was its longtime manager, whose corporate identity was secretary-treasurer, until it sold out to Fairmont Foods in 1930.

It bought and sold milk, cream and eggs and, in sum total, those small cream drafts issued from its stations along the railroad as far away as Ravenna and Merriman in Nebraska, Belle Fouche, Hill City, and Edgemont in South Dakota, and even Casper, Wyoming and Sterling, Colorado were lifesavers to many of the early farmers. Now, a popular piece of sarcasm resulting from boredom might be, "Let's go down and watch the Safeway truck unload." For years it had been "watch the trains come in" where a common part of the hectic scene of passenger, mail and baggage unloading was the several four-wheeled express trucks, pulled and guided by a heavy-duty hand tongue (and usually pushed as well by a couple of helpers) stacked two-high with five and ten gallon cans of cream, transported by rail on the baggage cars from those distant cream collecting points and destined for Alliance Creamery.

The principal product was butter – the Diamond A brand, in its distinctive yellow and white, one-pound package, was known all over Nebraska and in parts of neighboring states. The big butter output, however, was what was called "sweet butter" which contained no salt and was therefore acceptable and in demand by the Jewish people in the east. More than a carload of sweet butter was shipped every week, in wooden tubs held together by metal strapping, to New York City. Each shipment returned a large check to the company – and a favorable trade balance.

Everything in the butter and ice cream departments was spic and span clean. Of course, periodically there was a "visit" by some state or federal health authority, but there was not the bureaucratic control or picky interference to impede the processing, nor was it needed. On one occasion, Nels Jensen, an old Dane schooled in old country dairy cleanliness, was conducting the writer through his butter-making domain. He was the Chief and it was a neat and impressive overture to acquaint the young fellow from the front office with his art. We happened to pass a door where a number of cans of cream awaited to be used, emptied and routed back to wet lessor areas of the building for washing and return to the supplier. Old Nels stopped, jerked the lid from a can and tasted with his "dipping finger" its contents. He spat disgustedly with an exclamation "Bah, cow sh--!" and refused the whole lot. The young fellow was impressed but wonders to this day what disposition was made of that lot after he left.

Other dairy products processed were cottage and cream cheese; buttermilk containing a "starter" formula that had some therapeutic value; and several different flavors of ice cream and sherbets.

The ice making area was fascinating. Huge, heavy-duty metal containers were filled with water after being lowered or "nested" into place for freezing. When frozen the containers were raised, tipped and the large 300 pound cakes slid out of the container's end onto a slick ramp and were guided deftly by a man with tongs into an "ice room" where the temperature was held cold enough that there was practically no melting. (It would have been disastrous to have to handle manually 600 pounds or more had the cakes or blocks frozen together.) The need for muscle, quick reflexes and "know how" was very apparent. Ice was sold from the adjoining dock at retail in any size block to the drive-up customer. Weight was determined by the man's trained eye measurement. The larger blocks, weighing 300 pounds were usually sold at wholesale rates to "ice men" who peddled ice over town or to the railroad for refrigeration cars – before mechanical refrigeration was used.

In about 1932 the creamery expanded into the poultry business. Chickens were killed, dressed, frozen and sold. On one occasion, several years after his employment with the creamery, the writer intercepted some call ducks that a "hard up" farmer had brought in before they made the kill room. The use of live decoys was permitted for duck hunting although that was the last year they were legal. Those "callers" were a couple of pounds smaller than the ordinary domestic duck so the poultry manager was glad to unload them to a few of us hunters. They sure were loud and loquacious but provided a lot of spice to our hunting in the fall.

To encourage growers and to insure a dependable supply of turkeys, the creamery would enter into a contract with farmers under which the creamery would furnish fertile eggs and "carry" the grower until early fall, when the mature birds were processed and hopefully make the markets by the holiday season.

Herding turkeys was not too popular with the farmer, who often had to submit to derisive turkey calls from his "friends" with whom he earned about the same status as a sheep herder in a cattle country. At any rate, poultry raising in Nebraska, particularly turkeys, could not compete economically with the milder weather of southern states, notably Arkansas, and although many carloads of chickens were processed and shipped in the late thirties, the poultry division eventually was phased out of Alliance as was the processing of dairy products as the new owner, Fairmont, found it had other plants blessed with larger and better developed "milk sheds." Ice cream making went to Grand Island, cheese making to Denver and the milk and cream business that was left to Mitchell, Nebraska. And so ended an era – one of the most beneficial creations in the saga of Alliance industrial development.

A few farmers recognized the need for, and their opportunity, to supply milk in the city. Some fifteen dairies entered this business, some with delivery routes. About that time bureaucratic regulations for and education to the need for Grade A milk stirred a great health consciousness in the community. A local ordinance was adopted requiring compliance with U.S. and State health regulations including labeling and dating. It was of unquestionable benefit to human well-being but costly to the dairyman. Probably not more than a half dozen invested in acceptable milking parlors that would permit compliance with Grade A raw milk requirements. Health authorities much preferred complete pasteurization.

Yet another hurdle was thrown in the path of the local milk supplier and that was the milk carton. The large creameries preferred the milk carton, when it came into use, over the glass bottle. It was a convenience to supplier and purchaser alike in that the one became a throw-away; the other required washing and breakage certainly was an added expense. Fairmont had a jump on other suppliers which was almost monopolistic locally but its announced plan to commence milk deliveries in cartons would require ordinance revision by the city, if acceptable. In the delay entailed, the raw milk producers, operating under local permits, complained bitterly — they already owned their bottles and the paper containers would add a couple of cents to each unit. This, together with the fact they did not pasteurize, put them at a marketing disadvantage.

Fairmont had "tested the wind" so withdrew its carton plan in view of this uproar. Shortly afterwards, however, the problem was brought up again by a Grand Island creamery and Safeway's Lucerne brand which was being brought into the city. Fairmont had to follow. There were injunctions, an arrest developed, and with the complicated legal maneuvering, the situation took on the ludicrous appearance of a kangeroo court. The result was the big fellows outlasted the little fellows again, and now we have milk in cartons. In fact it is now so commonplace that a recent newspaper cartoon showing a small child asking "What is a milk bottle, Grandma?" is apropos.

Other manufacturing efforts developed since the thirties have been of a different nature and depended upon distant supplies and markets. The Jek Manufacturing plant was owned and operated by Lee Klesner but had an affiliation with the Goodall Company of Ogallala. It made capacitors and small parts for radios, televisions and other communications and was one of many such plants that sprang up over the nation to fill the demands of technology. Jek outgrew its birthplace, a relatively small machine shop located at Third and Platte, and moved to the old Alliance Creamery building which had become available. There it expanded, became equipped with more sophisticated equipment, provided a much appreciated payroll but was continually bandied about through ownership changes and affiliation with bigger companies such as Goodall Industries and TRW (Thompson, Raman and Woolridge). Finally it closed down when military demand eased and the government contracts, on which dozens of such plants depended, were no longer available. Locally the capacitor manufacture was a heyday while it lasted and payroll was a bonanza to the local economy in an otherwise difficult period.

Civic leaders were becoming concerned more and more with the lack of payrolls. The railroad was cutting down, the capacitor plant had "run its course," agriculture changes were taking place with the increase in irrigation but the municipal service expectancy – an appetite whetted by the airbase prosperity of World War II and its immediate post war years, could not be satisfied with a status quo economy. Alliance youth were leaving because there was nothing for them at home. As so often the case, need and necessity stimulate solutions and if credit can be given for a "brain child" which has since accomplished some industrial good and that long-sought payroll, it belongs to Clyde H. Sudman, then Vice-President and later President of the Guardian State Bank. The "Sudman Plan" involved acquiring a site that might be attractive to industry and which could possibly acquire financial help by issuing tax-free bonds under the State's new Industrial Development Act.

Alliance Development Corporation was formed and organized by a group of Alliance men in 1955 to provide a type of corporate identity to acquire land that could then be offered prospects in the community's efforts to attract new industry. Generally it was felt that the availability of a site for that use would attract payrolls. Land cost at least could be held to a reasonable figure and without the "padding" or "loading" of a profit to speculators. A prospect could get started and the site and the bond financing would be great pluses in getting industry to locate.

Stock was quickly subscribed to and paid for by 126 local firms and individuals. Its next step was the acquisition of a 97-acre tract just east of the city. Although the organization was separate and independent of local government, it had the blessings of and excellent cooperation from the City of Alliance in extending its water, sewer and electric utilities and from Box Butte County in zoning, which, of course, now is within the City's authority, and acceptance of the 1974 platting which included responsibility for certain roads within the industrial park as the need developed. Land acquisition by Nebraska Game and Parks District headquarters, True Temper Corporation, Electric Hose and Rubber Company, Western Potatoes, Inc., and Woolrich, Inc., has reduced the available area of the park to 43 acres, but through selective management, payrolls have been developed as originally planned and the Development Corporation is still in existence.

VII. Financial Institutions

The first two lots sold in the big 1887 auction were to financial and bank-to-be interests. Porter Eihlers and Company of Grand Island bought lot number one, at the corner of Third and Box Butte Avenue, where the Guardian State Bank and Trust Company is now loacted. This firm had a banking background and history and established a bank in a frame shack on that location. The second lot purchased was by the Bank of Alliance and was directly across the street north. Dr. F. M. Knight was its cashier. Later it merged into the Alliance National Bank on the southwest corner of the intersection with Dr. Knight as its president. So far banking history is legend to the writer; the twenties, he recalls from experience.

Four banks existed in the city then — the Alliance National, the Knight bank; the First National, headed by R. M. Hampton and later by Frank Abegg; the First State bank headed by Dr. H. A. Copsey and Charles Brittan; and the Guardian State Bank, headed by Sam Wright. During this period, especially about 1928-9, banking throughout the nation was a hazardous occupation due to the same causes that led up to the Great Depression, and to the numerous bank holdups that marked the lawless age of Dillinger, Ma Barker and her gang, Pretty Boy Floyd and many lesser criminal characters, who often were also identified with the illegal liquor trade. Fortunately, Alliance experienced no holdups although law enforcement officers are certain the town was "cased" on several occasions for a "job" that was never "pulled off." Unfortunately, it did experience two bank failures — one near the end of the decade and one shortly afterwards. But first — a sidelight . . .

Shortly after going to work for the Alliance National Bank in 1930, the writer was letting himself into the bank early one morning. The bank entrance was six or eight steps up from the sidewalk. When he was on the top step with key in the door, a voice behind him said, "Hold it. We'll go in with you." In a streak of bravado he pulled out the key and whirled around with a challenge of "Just who are we?" The irritated reply was "Didn't you ever see these bags (well-worn leather brief cases) before?" Of course he hadn't, but Fred Harris, Cashier, arrived about that time and introductions followed the "old home week" greetings between Fred and the two bank examiners. The young man felt very foolish but not nearly as much so then as after receiving Dr. Knight's scolding. No one was expected to risk his life refusing or trying to delay a holdup

Alliance National Bank. Note steps and popcorn wagon.

man—had the examiners been imposters. Perhaps the good doctor was a bit chagrined that the young bank clerk had almost had an experience, a holdup, which he, the doctor, had never had.

The First State Bank failed in mid-December 1929. The First National closed its doors October 31, 1931. Both institutions were victims of vicious whispering campaigns that never should have happened. Especially the latter, which was much larger in "totals" and which closing paralyzed the business economy in a large surrounding area. The Nebraska National Bank was formed primarily to "work out the paper" of that unfortunate bank, in which capacity it did a great and creditable job—any lending institution that could pay back its depositors on an 87% basis in those depressed years could not have been all bad. Subsequently, the Alliance National purchased the Nebraska National and moved into its building (formerly the First National location) on the northwest corner of the Third and Box Butte intersection. It was not until August 15, 1966 that the Alliance National Bank moved into its present new building at Third and Laramie Avenue. Meanwhile the Guardian State Bank purchased the old original Alliance National building which was razed to accommodate its beautiful new home.

The Guardian State Bank was purchased from the Wright interests, prior to the two failures, by the A. J. Abbott family.

47

"A. J.'s" sons, Chris and LeRoy were the principal owners but Chris spent little time with the bank. His ranching interests and national recognition serving on the boards of railroads, A. T. and T. and U.S. Chamber of Commerce kept him busy. So "A. J." selected Clyde Sudman, then a well known and promising young banker in Oshkosh, Nebraska, to become cashier and meld his practical banking experience with LeRoy's "school learned" but instinctive banking ability. The next forty years proved this a very wise decision. Both men became well identified over the entire state and LeRoy Abbott's stature grew nationwide as far as big city financial circles were concerned.

Today Alliance is blessed with two strong family banks. They have ridden out successfully recessions, depressions and competitive rivalry, but both have lent a powerful feeling of confidence to the community. F.D.I.C. is nice but the writer is a believer in earned trust and institutional responsibility.

Down memory lane recalls almost thirty years of home financing in Alliance without a local Building and Loan. Banks provided some interim help, but limitations in banking laws prevent a bank engaging, beyond a modest percent of its deposits, in the conventional longtime housing loan. This had to come from outside loaning institutions, a practice which realtors resorted to; but as this is written four building and loans (First Federal, Nile Valley, Commercial Federal, and Western Nebraska Savings) have built new offices and established themselves with the Alliance economy.

Three other financial institutions worthy of mention because of the surprising growth they have made and the benefits available through them to their members are the Alliance Railroad Employees Credit Union, the Box Butte Public Employees Federal Credit Union, and Consumers Cooperative Federal Credit Union.

The Alliance National Farm Loan Association, the Federal Land Bank, the Farm Home Administration, Federal Housing Administration and other federally identified institutions are now available in Alliance.

VIII. Agri-Organizations

Many other interests have organized in the Alliance area down through the years. Of those surviving we think of the Nebraska Stockgrowers first; first headed up by Alliance Postmaster and Rancher, Robert Graham; and the Nebraska Brand Committee, enabled by a creative law in about 1923. Both have permanent headquarters housed in their own buildings in Alliance.

Another agri-linked organization was the Nebraska Potato Growers. By the 1920's it was found that Box Butte County potatoes, initially raised on dry land farms but much later under irrigation, were in great demand as seed potatoes in the south. An association, The Nebraska Certified Potato Growers, was formed and directed by the late William Morrow, with a close association with the Nebraska College of Agriculture. Its purpose was certifying seed grown locally as disease free and to develop a dependable market for the crop. The "blue tag" became a symbol of assurance and dependability in the business. Some individuals grew two potato crops a year – the seed was raised around Alliance; the second crop in Texas or some other southern state.

Competition with such areas as Idaho, the Red River Valley in North Dakota, and Maine, plus transportation disadvantages, were always impediments to this costly-to-produce, harvest, and highly perishable product. The potato grown now is by mechanized and highly technical methods. Not all farmers can spend the time and investment on potato production and work it into their rotation practices, but those who have the equipment, cellars for storage and "know how" are usually well rewarded financially by this high income crop. The Association was reorganized in about 1962 and the sales and certification departments were separated.

So great a part of the farm economy was potato growing that the high school paper and yearbook were both known as the Spud, and the athletic teams were called the Spud-Pickers.

In these early years, the Sioux Indian were confined to the Pine Ridge and Rosebud reservations in South Dakota. They were objects of curiosity on Alliance streets, except at summer circuses and rodeos and during the potato harvest in fall. They would be excused then from the reservation to pick potatoes in Box Butte County. If they had not returned by shortly after the first killing frost, the Indian Agency came looking for them. This situation continued for years until about World War II when the government relaxed such restrictions, permitted the Indian to leave the reservation, vote if registered, purchase and consume alcoholic liquor, and enjoy full citizenship if he chose. 49

IX. Wars and Police Actions

Alliance history has spanned three wards and innumerable "police actions" which would have been a shocking reaction to Thomas Jefferson were he here today. Bless his soul, he would have endorsed the Civil War to settle our internal differences, and the Revolutionary War to defend our country and fight for its rights, but he would have been hesitant to approve the Spanish American War and outright opposed World War I and World War II and the several police actions we have since pursued on foreign soil.

This writer recalls only three veterans of the Civil War – Robert Garret the oldest member of the Garret family, prominent in early Alliance history, and a crusty old fellow, always on crutches, by name of Colonel Evans, and a grey-haired darky whose name cannot be recalled. The first two were remembered for a place in a horse-drawn buggy and later in a touring car without side curtains in Alliance patriotic parades and spectacular events like July 4. Evans would make a patriotic speech with the slightest provocation but was unpredictable and hard to handle. He never seemed affronted by being omitted but his whole life was one of mental torment so he probably just went into one of his appropriate moods for the occasion. Melissa Dickey was a kindly old lady reputed to have been widowed in the Civil War.

The Spanish American War of 1898 was fought to help the Cubans from the clutches of Spain. This war had the least impact on Alliance history but its veterans never let the patriotic fires burn low. Veterans of this war included E. G. Laing, Perry Law, James Hilton, Ed Henry and Monte Gebhart. There were a few others but these are remembered, probably because they sported a place in the flag bearer ranks and a noisy bugler in all parades and patriotic celebrations.

World War I was an emotional conflict. Perhaps the dominant nationality in the entire state was German. There were many mixed feelings about entering the conflict but the sinking of the Lusitania by German U-Boats and the continual emphasis attached to violating neutrality laws, provided the hysteria needed to cause our declaration of war on Germany April 6, 1917.

Captain Jack Miller of the State National Guard organized Company G locally. The writer, then at age of ten, dressed in his best "blue serge" and sporting a large white First Liberty Loan button on his lapel, watched the swearing in and roll call process in the old fireman armory building and when he wasn't saluting every flag on the way to the depot to see those heroes off, he was checking his steps with the company's cadence. We are certain that, individually, they all became better marchers after a few months at Camp Cody, New Mexico, where they trained until sent to France in 1918.

The returning veterans formed the American Legion as mentioned elsewhere in this account. It also had an auxiliary. The writer never has been too sure of his ground on Veterans of Foreign Wars but there was a difference in the policies of these two service organizations which I am sure each had merit in their own philosophies. The Soldiers Bonus Act, under which veterans were paid for participation in the war was passed and they were paid in 1936. Its benefits probably came in handy to the veteran but the writer cannot recall that the impact had any great effect on local economy, as many thought it would, and he is sure it didn't cover the loss of time, life, and other heartaches resulting from the great conflict.

The surprise attack on Pearl Harbor by the Japanese December 7, 1941, shocked the entire country into a highly emotional reaction to start World War II. Backing up the President, the congress voted 470 to 1 to declare war. The oft-quoted Japenese Admiral that said "We may have just awakened a sleeping giant" put the situation very accurately.

In mid-March 1942 a site board of air force and engineering officers with one civilian, the country's only glider expert as the U.S. hadn't kept up with Hitler's youth who had received the training and encouragement for many years in aero-dynamics and dominated the world as far as glider "know how" was concerned, arrived in Alliance. This board spent two days in Alliance checking on its natural flight advantages and inherent assets and receiving the city council's commitment to acquire a specific area, for lease in turn to the government. The next two months were shrouded in military secrecy but on June 10 the War Department announced that construction was authorized for an Air Support and Glider Training Base at Alliance, Nebraska. Several politicians and prominent men have implied and hinted, or if so credited have not denied, that it was their clout that influenced the decision to locate the base at Alliance. The writer has a different conviction – that it was that new power plant with its 2500 kw surplus capacity that swung the decision and paved the way for unbridled profiting for the next few years. That had the clout.

The City purchased some 3261 acres of land for slightly under $30.00 per acre ($96,847.61 to be exact) about four miles southeast of town; and leased 2900 acres to the federal government for twenty-five years with a clause in the contract requiring the government to restore the land to its former state and condition when returned to the city. Accepting the runways, buildings and utilities and personal property in lieu of restoration; and benefiting from a generous gesture in the form of outright gifts and the priority position of a municipality for salvaged materials to help with the cost of maintaining the giant facility, was a business in itself in the late forties. In the next thirty years, the vast airport operation was carried on with salvage sales and rentals paying the way and without any taxes being levied for airport purposes.

The base was constructed under the Missouri River Engineers Corps' direction at a cost varying from twenty to twenty-five million dollars – rather a generous spread but it is as close as can be ascertained. Everything was rush, rush, rush. For instance, the long runways were deemed necessary for glider take offs but before the third runway was completed the C-47's were towing three gliders at once and using about a third of a runway length.

Altogether there were included more than 600 buildings and complete water, sewer and electric distribution systems. The facilities were designed for training glider infantrymen, engineers, artillery, medics and the spectacular paratroops – often referred to as our suicide fighting arm. All were used in some theatre of operation over the world.

The arrival of the first trainees was amusing. Both the Glider Infantry and the Paratroopers came from Fort Benning, Georgia, to Alliance. The infantry arrived first, probably two weeks in advance, and really had the Paratroopers' reputations made for them upon their arrival. The townspeople actually viewed the Paratroopers arrival with apprehension, but actually no serious trouble ever developed by either. The same could not be said for other towns in the vicinity. Some of those places were practically "taken apart" by the soldiers lucky enough to secure a weekend pass.

Some 20,000 trained here. For that many, varied entertainment was important and was provided to maintain morale among the spirited, and sometimes bored or lonely, young soldiers. Joe Louis, then heavyweight champion, sparred in exhibitions, comedians, singers and other entertainers were brought in. On one occasion a large bus was chartered for a trip to Denver and returned with a hundred young colored girls. The company of colored service troops was not overlooked. The Officers' Club on the Base was a social center for personnel and invited people from the city.

In town, the old city hall was razed and a new frame U.S.O. building erected. Townswomen responded with an active U.S.O. organization and kept things interesting for the enlisted men. The clubs practically threw the doors open to service men. Little abuse resulted from all the activity and there were very few places ever placed "off limits" to military personnel. Wives and other camp followers really placed a burden on the town for housing. There was hardly a home that didn't rent one or several rooms or apartments. There were few garages and even barns and chicken houses that were not made into living quarters, if they were not too bad, for these people. The city's population zoomed and was estimated to exceed 12,000.

The day of reckoning approached and 1944 found all air trained personnel in undisclosed foreign camps. Most from the Alliance base went to England and were principals in the big show on D Day. Mortality was terribly high. We have heard of figures like 85% with the 507th Paratroopers. The valor displayed and documented touched all local people who, in a few short years, had become close to and almost endeared by those young men who trained hard, fought hard and died on a beach, torn and maimed often beyond comprehension.

This was the home front but it is not to say Alliance did not contribute its share of native sons and manpower to the military; and in all theatres of operation, the Pacific, Africa and Europe; and in all branches of service – land, sea and air. It might also be noted three Alliance men, Paul Thompson, Frank Dailey, and Earl Barnes became generals during World War II.

The Second Air Force took over command of the base after the First Troop Carrier left late in 1944 and flew from it until its deactivation in 1945. And what happened to that enormous installation? Well, after "the in lieu of restoration" clause was settled, War Assets Administration had the responsibility for the disposition and sale of 485 buildings and personal property not turned to the city. General Services then superseded War Assets in the final disposal. The quit claim deed breaking the 25-year lease also contained the conveyance to the city an additional five quarter sections of government-owned land.

X. The Automobile

Now let us drop back from the foregoing subject, which the writer has developed so close to today, to the automobile. Alliance did not escape its effect on every day life in the revolution of living habits, manners and morals that take place after any war, but World War I in this case. The car fit nicely (?) into the picture with prohibition and the post War I pleasure-seeking ventures common to the twenties.

It has been documented somewhere that in 1919 only 10% of all cars produced in the U.S. were closed (sedans or coupes); by 1927 the percentage of closed cars manufactured reached 82.8%. The closed car was protection from the weather, a means of escaping parents or chaperons temporarily, and from the influence of neighborhood opinion. In Frederick Lewis Allen's book ONLY YESTERDAY, a juvenile judge was quoted as branding the automobile as being "a house of prostitution on wheels."

Well, be that as it may, the development of the automobile and the various garages in Alliance is interesting. The garage replaced the livery barn of which Alliance always had three or four. Here mounts and teams were stabled by the day, week, or for "open end" periods with board and room—oats and hay, and a stall. Rentals of more-or-less dependable saddle horses, buggies and rigs and wagons were also available.

One of the last livery barns belonged to the Phillips family at First and Laramie Avenue. It burned to the ground one winter night in the early twenties during Christmas vacation. The next morning provided a most revolting scene of bloated carcasses of 22 horses that perished being skinned and butchered on a fresh eight inch snow that had fallen during the night by some reservation Indians that were still in the area.

Except for an old abandoned 1901 Oldsmobile parked for years on a vacant lot on West Third Street, neglected, vandalized and in a needed state of repair and depreciation, my memory of cars is pretty much limited to the Model T Ford which the company built from 1908-1927. This is probably because that make, in a touring model, was the one Cy Laing finally mustered the nerve to buy. It was complete with isinglass side curtains and demountable tire rims. The family had a barrel of enjoyment with it—fishing, hunting, camping trips and just Sunday drives. The one near-casualty recalled was when the family dog, that insisted on perching atop the front fender, went off over the front end and was run over with no more serious damage than a few bruises and sore spots.

One incident that Cy probably never was aware of was that, loaded with members of a small orchestra and with a bass drum strapped on its back, it set a gravel road speed record one night (22 miles) from the Hemingford dance hall to the Maryland Cafe in Alliance. The "musical son" might be slightly mistaken, but it seems the time was 35 minutes.

In turn, for the son, came the Model A sedan and in 1934 a V-8. There have been others since but those three models seem indelible in his memory.

"Henry" sure kept his promise in those years, when he provided better wages and made such strides in mass production – that he would never bring out a new model without lowering the price of the Ford.

Chevrolet history with General Motors was so involved with Durants, Oaklands, Cadillacs and others, before being made really big by one Alfred P. Sloan, that memory is hazy.

Early day dealers and the "makes" they offered include Link Lowery and Ed Henry (Dodge, Star and Studebaker), A. H. Jones (Chrysler and Plymouth), Robert Cobb (Buick), Nicoli (Nash and Reo) and Coursey and Miller and then G. C. Richardson and later Abegg and Turner, then Cover-Jones (Ford). There were others, of course, like Sturgeon, Rumer, Wallace Auto and Truck, Keeler and Miller that for one reason, then another, were shorter lived.

Lowery and Henry garage just after roof garden was enclosed.

XI. Dance Crazed

One notable monument left by the early day garage people was the Lowery and Henry garage at Fifth and Box Butte Avenue. It was a modern brick and cement structure, complete with an open air roof garden on the second floor. With this feature it became the most popular dance floor in town and Alliance was truly a dance-crazed town in those days. Initially, Bill Edwards' local orchestra established itself as the "home band" but there were also many traveling bands such as Morrisons, a colored band from Denver, booked into the Garden. This orchestra in particular had a lot of class and its rendition of "Three O'Clock in the Morning" played as the midnight sign off with a touching chorus by four violins still causes goose pimples in wistful remembrance.

Other dance halls of the early thirties and before included the Roundhouse, Dutch Mill, Coursey's Hall, and the Firemen's Armory in town; and Curry's, Kastner's Barn and Sleepy Hollow in the country. The latter was a dairy barn north of town, owned by a man named Bliss, that splurged for several summers with Link Dunn's orchestra playing out of Lincoln.

BIG BAND ERA. Herbie Smith's Orchestra. Circa 1934. Zumwalt, H. Smith, Salisbury, Cremin, Threlkeld, C. Smith, Ballard, Laing and Irwin.

For the rest of the more than two decades that dancing was so popular, local bands furnished the music. The Whaley Brothers (Harv and Todd), the Smith Brothers (Rich, Harold and Charles) and individual bands that included such names as Alter, Rathburn, Cogswell, Threlkeld, Cremin, Robins and the writer are just a few of the musicians that one time or another played under such fancy names as the Yellow Jackets, Red Feather Entertainers, not to mention Hut's Hot Hokum Hounds (Anderson) and then there was Minnie Wiker and Stubby Jones, bless their hearts.

This crazy era began to taper off in intensity after a roof was constructed over the Garden and its maple wood floor was ruined by the then management promoting roller skating as well as dancing. Other influences of note were taking place. Prohibition's end was approaching and the clubs, with their plush furniture, nickelodeons bringing big band perfection right to their comfortable upholstered lounges and "bottle clubs," were taking "the fun" (risk) away from the days of the flask.

XII. Other Entertainment

Alliance may have been a "have not" community for many natural material assets but ingenuity was never lacking in making the most of its natural environment.

The old Phelan Opera House (above the present Rhoads and Gamble stores) provided the stage for many traveling shows as well as the home talent productions such as Tom Thumb Weddings, Womanless Weddings and a number of Lavender and Old Lace type shows long before Little Theatre , which capped its many small productions with the World Premier of "Old Jules" in 1938, was conceived. It seems the town was always blessed with a movie house – the Empress, Rialto, Alliance and the Fox Imperial where the Pathe News was a regular item and a weekly vaudeville show and a shoot'em-up Western provided the usual movie going menu. Chautauquas, and tent shows like Arlingtons and others providing nightly changes in drama, were popular as were the large circuses and carnivals. Sometimes these repeated a stand for a second time in a summer. All contributed to fill an entertainment void. Who cared about Broadway?!

XIII. Outdoor Recreation

Two Auburn hunters have luck near Alliance, circa 1928.

Hay Springs men hunt near Alliance, circa 1912, Scheffner, Richmond and Goff.

Before irrigation started the lowering trend to the area's water table and the great drouth of the thirties, the sandhill lakes always contained water, at least enough to create a flyway for migrating waterfowl. Within an hour's drive from town was excellent duck and goose shooting and often fishing. Limits were very lenient and upland hunting (grouse) was equally attractive. The gaudy pheasant, while being stocked in counties along the Platte, did not show up in Box Butte County until the very early thirties.

A nice day's hunt in early thirties. Sampson, Vogel, O'Bannon and Sanderson.

Outdoor entertainment was always dominant in the area. In the early years of the century footracing was very popular and each community had its "pride and joy" on which both small and large wagers were not unusual. Horse racing in the teens was also popular, including many spirited and competitive harness races. And, it might be said that betting was not limited to men's footracing. Shreves, Mohlring and Boag were familiar names in the harness sport and Lightfoot, a white stocking bay, was an exceptional pacer and never was beaten to the writer's knowledge. Alvie Bullock and Dwight Zediker were names connected more with riding. Rodeos, as Stockmens Convention programs came to be called, and baseball, provided a lot of participant and spectator entertainment. There was many a discussion on pronunciation—whether it was r-o-d-e-o' or r-o-da'-o. It is too bad that the big baseball scouts didn't get to see some of the early local talent. In some sports they apparently did for we recall, for instance, the Herian brothers performed in Europe and Madison Square Garden in the rodeo art of roping, bulldogging and bronc busting.

Cruising Box Butte Avenue, 1916 style.

As better organization was dictated by lack of community programing, and as the County Fairgrounds was located in Hemingford, the Alliance Amusement park was conceived, promoted and built on the newly acquired "Nation Quarter" about 1927. Its corporate structure was sparked by Ben Sallows and LeRoy Abbot and with permanent grandstands it became the established location during the thirties for most of the community promotions up until such activities found a new home at Sandhillo. This was the name given by the sandhill ranchers and townspeople promoting parimutuel racing to new facilities at the airport. Sandhillo's corporate identity was the Box Butte Agriculture and Breeding Association. That implied it had something to do with agriculture and brought it into compliance technically with the State's racing laws. This legalized sport, rigidly controlled under State supervision flourished from 1953 for years. Its facilities on the former Airbase site became the location for rodoes, roping events and practically all outdoor entertainment, least of all being the annual 4th of July fireworks displays.

Broncho Lake was located two miles west of Alliance and was a huge expanse of water fed by springs and inlets from the Snake Creek valley beyond and to the west. It had no outlet, therefore its water was strong of alkali and salts. Fish could not survive it. However, when full, it furnished swimming, boating and great hunting. One of the first promotions of its immeasurable potential was the construction and launching of Bedelia, a large paddlewheel boat with a capacity of about fifty persons. Jim Miller, later to become the County Sheriff, operated the boat on this unusually large saucer of water which was a mile in diameter and has been measured to eight feet in depth. The modest fare for the ride was most popular. Bedelia also served as the launching site for several spectacular fireworks demonstrations on July 4, but it finally swamped, was neglected and completely abandoned.

Of longer duration and even greater utilization of Broncho was the swimming. The city did not have a pool until 1935, since the indoor pool originally in the Firemen's Armory had been discontinued and replaced with a dance floor. It was not public anyhow. So Broncho Lake was the scene of many "beach parties." So much so that at one time there were three piers constructed and extended into the lake for diving and docking of boats. Two, the municipal and the Boy Scouts, had bath houses that were used prolifically, in spite of Dr. H. A. Copsey's annual August admonishment to the community that "the water in Broncho Lake is contaminated and unfit for swimming."

The third pier served even a greater use and multi-purpose as the Alliance Country Club was organized and incorporated in 1923. It had a nice little nine-hole golf course which was immediately "taken to" by most of its one hundred original stockholders, several of whom acquired such names as "Two-club Bill" (W. D. Rumer) and P. J. the mashie masher" (Father P. J. Manning, who usually shunned tournaments and club championship play, but who with about four clubs and his cricket style of play had no peer on the course.)

The club's pier was lighted and served as a dock for boats and canoes. In 1925 the clubhouse burned completely to the ground and in the conflagration, nineteen factory-built canoes and several boats in winter storage were, of course, completely destroyed and never replaced. The clubhouse was completely rebuilt on the same site and exactly as the original structure. Golf, tennis, dancing and the usual activities of a social club life continued. The latter, with its

Bronco Lake and approach from east to Country Club.

Alliance Country Club, 1923

exclusive characteristic, was probably the chief reason for the promotion and establishment of a second golf course closer to town, available to the greens fee player, and therefore considerably less expensive and more democratic. The Junior Chamber of Commerce was responsible for it. The town just couldn't support two courses and eventually both became grossly underfinanced and were discontinued.

The country club, after a short period of leasing the dine and-dance concession and several reorganizations, was sold by its remaining eighteen stockholders to a private individual, B. B. Wright. Today it is operated as a supper club under its original name — Alliance Country Club — by Lyle A. Hare.

Boating changed for the most part to a spectator sport with motorboat races a regular Sunday entertainment. Schadwinkel, Schafer, and Essay were a few of the names prominent in the very competitive sport. Bigger and bigger motors propelling the same boat (not designed for the additional power) often contributed to some ludicrous performances as those "dry land sailors" zealously competed for their wins and records.

XIV. Remember When

President Teddy Roosevelt spoke from the platform of his private railroad car at the depot in Alliance.

Alliance had a brickyard. Ruins of the kilns and storage barn, south of the railroad wye and west of the south portion of Black Hills Avenue now being vacated for Burlington Northern expansion, existed until just a few years ago. Practically every building in any direction from Second and Box Butte Avenue was initially built of this native brick. It was fireproof but too soft for any durability and eventually had to be "faced up" with a better and harder imported brick. The paving brick on Box Butte Avenue and Third Street (now overlaid with asphalt) was imported from Kansas.

Madam Schumann-Heink made a personal appearance singing at the Imperial Theatre during World War I, a time when anti-German feeling ran high and the possibility of her pro-German allegiance was in the minds of her audience.

Some of the best ice skating, except for the indoor rink in the BEMI building at the airport which came much later, was on the widened areas through the rutted trail in the normally shallow swale that ran diagonal across the then vacant lots from Second and Big Horn Avenue southwesterly to the O'Bannon (now Neuswanger) elevator. The area was bounded on the south by coal sheds along the "city" switch track and belonged to various lumber yards (Foster, Forest, Dierks and Sacks) now long-removed to make room for the City's power plant expansion.

William Cody, Buffalo Bill, would invariably show up with an Indian act in Sells Flota Circus and in the circus parade would team up with a Captain Hardy, a Remington Arms representative, and shoot blue rocks from the rear seat of a moving touring car. They seldom missed—thus demonstrating the company's gun powder and bullet perfection.

The old junk man who would drive Alliance streets in a one-horse drawn cart calling out "Any rags, any old bones, any scrap today Lady?" That was Daniel Hill. From his very unglamorous occupation, he was able to one day buy an abandoned potash plant in Antioch, Nebraska, from Northwestern Metal Company, liquidate the plant's salvage and one later day his family would sell considerable property to the University of Nebraska for stadium and campus parking lots in Lincoln.

The old wooden Burlington depot burned down November 24, 1906 and was replaced with the present passenger depot in 1908. The waiting room in the new building was quite ornamental and included two wall-mounted fountains animated by a constant flow of water circulated from the appendages of two cherubs. That was art! As this is written, the Burlington Northern is making plans for razing the depot for a parking area.

The Elks Club was organized with its first clubrooms upstairs in the Reddish block.

People with a contagious disease were quartered in a "Pest House" just east of South Alliance. Medical science then advanced to the quarantine of the infested home by placard, and finally the practice was apparently abandoned, or else we have advanced to complete control of the spread of the "dreaded diseases" like measles, smallpox, chicken pox, mumps, diphtheria, scarlet fever and others.

The city dump was almost any place along the east side draw that has become the determinant in the pattern of the city park system. As the town expanded, dumping was without direction— footing excavation for the City's substation at Eleventh and Hudson was greatly complicated by the unearthing of long-covered bedsprings. This went on until a dump was established just south of the East Third Street overpass. In 1927 this dump was moved to the southeast corner of the "Nation Quarter" and after many years was managed as to justify the better sounding designation of a "sanitary fill."

The post office was located in the old Alliance National Bank building. Martin Brennan recalls how the kids would go "hookin'" (attaching sleds to anything capable of towing them), get all wet and go into the post office dripping to dry off and get warm on the steam radiators which were a novelty in themselves. Judge Ira Tash was postmaster and never ran them out. The present post office was moved from that site to the new building constructed in 1914.

Mary White Belly from the Reservation, was a perennial winner in the greased pig contest at Fall Festival occasions.

Promotions other than dancing in the Lowery-Henry roof garden included auto shows and athletic events. Wrestling, before the day of rasslin', was popular. Local prides included A. B. Wheeler, Steve Cannon, Ray Trabert to name a few; but cards also often included such notables as Joe Stecker, John Pesek, Ray Steele (then using another name) and Charles Peters. Probably the best local boxer of a later date was a heavyweight by name of Motley, but before him were such local prides as Francis O'Conner and Mel Wyland. On one occasion, the well-known Billie Papke was imported with a dampening effect on any aspirations of the latter.

J. C. McCorkle would bet any and all a new hat that it would rain July 6. There were times that a heavy dew saved him and, of course, there were times that he lost but all-in-all, J. C. had a great many hats.

The Rumer Building was located on the northeast corner of the Third and Box Butte intersection, now a vacant lot. It once housed Brennan's Drug Store and later Montgomery Wards Retail Store. It had a wide stairway off Box Butte Avenue. Upstairs were several offices but mostly that second floor was noted for the bachelor apartments it contained. Many bizarre happenings took place there. On one occasion, "the sports" had ordered a late supper to be catered from Cy Laing's Silver Grill prior to an early morning departure for hunting. Cy delivered the heaping tray himself and found a bunch of drunks, if his practiced eyes ever beheld such. Several had their hunting clothes on and were "ready" at that hour. Jimmy Graham had on his breast waders and just as Cy was leaving after the delivery, there was a loud shot heard. Thinking a bad accident must have happened, Cy ran back into the room only to find that Jimmy had just shot out the street lamp in front of the old city hall! No accident – just a pretty good shot from about seventy yards.

Western Nebraska was still digging out of the drifts and effects of the blizzard of 1949 when KCOW (k-cow) radio station received permission from the Federal Communications Commission to "go on the air" February 15, 1949. Founded by the Sandhills Broadcasting Company, a strictly local organization led by Hans Jaggers, Wharton Cover, William Morrow, and Walter R. Metz, "the voice of Alliance" sounded more than welcome to the marooned ranchers and farmers of the Nebraska Panhandle.

Back in about 1920 to 1923, Howard (now Doctor) Cogswell and the writer were more or less "going steady" and breaking into the dance orchestra game. A typical Saturday night after a three-hour playing stint at the Roof Garden, would probably include blowing too big a part of the night's pay for a ham salad sandwich and a thick malted milk homestyle at Jim DeBerry's Alliance Candy Company. Then it was home to Cogswell's where we would sit for hours with head phones on listening to some of the clear channel radio stations that were on the air at those early morning hours. Coon and Sanders, the Kansas City Nighthawks, was one of our favorites along with "Boy" Blue from St. Louis and the big name bands, Isham Jones, Ben Bernie and others from Chicago. During the following week we almost set the neighbors crazy trying to imitate some novel passage that we heard on the air before Lula, Howard's mother, came downstairs, awakened two sleeping young fellows and sent them off to bed.

XV. Reminiscent Graffiti

The "Peep Sights" was Ben Sallows' personal column in the *Times & Herald*. In it he tested "editorial privilege." The writer subscribed to the paper while in University; and as fraternity brothers caught on to its caustic barbs, he often returned to the house from classes to find his paper almost dog-eared by the brothers who had discovered the humorous and sometimes brutal barbs contained in the column.

So it was with Dr. Knight's experience while drilling with the Home Guards during World War I. Doctor was an exercise bug. One early evening drill included a parade in which a column left was made at Third and Box Butte in the mud from a recent rain. The good Doctor lost a rubber in making the turn and broke ranks to retrieve it. Sallows "peeped up" the incident. Doctor Knight was so provoked that he didn't speak to Ben until the bank crisis in 1931 dictated that old grudges be buried in the public interest.

Billy King was about a 300-pound, long-time saloon keeper. During the World War I potash boom a group of Alliance men formed the Alliance Potash Company and built a plant to refine the valuable chemical in Antioch. Billy was almost a nuisance with his incessant requests to become a stockholder. Somehow when the initial investment money was needed he hadn't been asked. He hounded Fred Harris at the bank for a chance to get in on the goodies. Fred always said "Billy, there is no stock available, it is a closed corporation." On November 11, 1918 the Armistice was signed, the war was over, and the first production of the plant was loaded for shipment at Newport News, Virginia, but was worthless. The Alliance Potash Company was "holding the bag" and, of course, went broke. The morning after the news was received, Billy stuck his head in the bank door and said, "Fred, thanks. I didn't know before what you meant by a 'closed corporation'."

Earl Mallery and Henry Fricke served together as city councilmen. Mayor Earl subsequently resigned to accept the appointment of city manager. Fricke, a building contractor, became mayor. A couple of years later, it was discovered as construction was completed that Fricke had built a house on a vacant lot owned by Mallery but located next to a Fricke-owned lot. The two men were not overly friendly anyhow and the terms of the settlement between them remains one of the town's best kept secrets.

Johnny King, Billie's son, was a better-than-average baseball pitcher, enough so that he was given a tryout with the Chicago White Sox. Johnny was very modest and self-effacing person, who always had time to visit with the writer – probably relating his interesting experiences was rewarding to him by the wide-eyed, awestruck hero worship returned. Once he was asked about that big league experience. "Well, 'little Cy' (as he usually called me) I was there and there were an awful lot of good ball players there – I just stayed for coffee."

In the presidential election of 1916 Doctor Knight, an ardent republican, backed Charles E. Hughes with a $1,000 wager with one Charley Tully, an equally loyal democrat. It appeared Hughes had won the very close election and the Doctor, like the rest of the nation went to bed thinking he had won. By morning, with the west coast returns in, Wilson and a jubilant Mr. Tully were winners in a very close race.

William Mitchell, at about 5'6", 120 pounds and with a quick temper and an unbridled feistiness that was characterized by habitual nervous snorts and a sniffing, was regarded as the best defense attorney in western Nebraska. At least, he was the most feared. He was a scourge to young lawyers, aggressive and abusive to all in the courtroom. One day a very scared and excited cowboy burst into his office exclaiming, "Mr. Mitchell, the sheriff has a warrant out for me for shooting at Archie Phillips! Will you take my case?" "Did you shoot at him?" asked Billy. "Well, yes, but just to scare him" was his reply. "Will you please defend me?" "Of course (snort! sniff!), of course," Mitchell replied. "It ain't a crime to shoot a Phillips in Box Butte County!"

When the Country Club was sold in 1947 by its stockholders to B. B. Wright, Fred Harris was secretary of the organization. As he went to imprint the corporate seal on the deed, it was noticed that the seal was that of the Benevolent and Protective Order of Elks, Alliance Lodge No. 961. A hurried call was made to Percy Cogswell, longtime secretary of the Elks Lodge. He had a wrong seal in his club files, so an exchange was quickly made and the correct seal attached. Both men wondered how many instruments that went out of Fred's bank had been made "legal" by the seal of the fraternal organization.

Bernard Phelan's news stand was located on Third Street in the Alliance National Bank building. It boasted a small radio and was a natural meeting place for some of the town's leading citizens to kill the rest of the noon hour after eating lunch downtown. Occasionally, as in this instance, some time "was stolen" to listen to a football game. This day in 1925 it was Nebraska playing Illinois

69

at Urbana and was particularly interesting to the gathering because Frank Dailey, a local high school star of a couple of years earlier, although not a starter was on the squad. Early Mallery, an ardent Dailey fan and fraternity brother, was late arriving at the news stand. The radio announced Dailey's substitution into the game just as Mallery breathlessly arrived. "I'll bet $100 he scores!" cried the hysterical Mallery. Of course everyone wanted a piece of that and in no time at all the bet was covered just as Daily intercepted a pass and ran for a touchdown. Nebraska won that day 14-0, but the zaniest play of all was made in Alliance.

It was in 1950 at a Rotary Club dinner meeting, the night before a city council meeting at which bids had been invited on Alliance's first parking meters. The writer was privileged that night to share a table with three attorneys. The subject was brought up and the then city manager, sneaky as he was, sort of let it slip that a salesman for one of the companies had engaged Harry Gantz to appear at the meeting as the company's "local representative." Harry admitted it, adding that he had met the fellow once as a lobbiest in the legislature. That was all the other two lawyers needed to start the kidding. They assured the CM that it would be right handy, knowing Harry as I did, to be able to call him about mealtime or whenever a meter stuck or was otherwise out of order "to get his little bag of tools and get right down and fix it." After all he represented the meter company. W. R. Metz and R. O. Reddish poured it on unmercifully. Harry called Mr. Goldsberry right after the meeting to get another representative – he resigned.

In the mid-thirties Dean Taylor was the rector of the Episcopal Church. He was a rotund little bachelor, quick with a retort and quite popular with the younger blades around town. One night, actually it was early morning, the Dean and several friends had just finished a midnight snack at the Alliance Hotel Cafe and were at the front desk settling up for the meal. Joe Smith, the proprietor of a pool hall at Second and Box Butte, entered in a slight state of inebriation. Joe announced, "Hold up there, Dean Taylor, I'm buying for everyone in the house!" The Dean said, "Sorry, Joe, I just paid for mine." Joe wanted to do something for the man of the cloth so countered, "Well what can I do for you, anything you want or need up at the church?" "Well, yes," replied Taylor, thinking quickly of a most improbable fulfillment, "We do need a ton of coal or so." No one present figured Joe's memory would last that long but come Monday morning, one of the lumber yards delivered a load of coal to the Episcopal Church, compliments of Joe Smith.

One time the Elks Club promoted a rather outstanding boxing card at the Roof Garden. The main event involved for one a black heavyweight of some repute, who showed up several weeks early. He really impressed the "brothers" as he worked out in their gym. His muscles rippled and the sweat poured off him as he worked the bag, shadow boxed and did sprints around the gym. Some didn't even care to see the unfortunate opponent of such an impressive speciman and placed bets sight unseen accordingly. By time for the first preliminary, the other principal had not shown up. The committee was desperate. Someone thought of former police chief, Cy Laing, who knew all the drifters and might have an idea. In jail at the time was a yellow skinned mulatto laying out a fine for vagrancy or equally minor offense because he had no money to pay a fine. The police magistrate was handy and went along with Cy's assurance that they could get rid of this boarder if he was willing to fight. "Boy, would you be willing to fight a man tonight and then get right out of town afterwards?" asked Cy. The answer was affirmative. Quickly the committee got him some trunks, transferred him to the scene of battle. He made the ring in just the nick of time. The announcer coined some sort of introduction, the fighters met in the center and received their instructions, returned to their respective corners and with the sound of the gong "the favorite" sprang across the ring, then mercifully decided to dance and shadow box a little first – he only got that one mistake. The jail bird, or ex-jail bird, nailed him with one punch sending him clear through the ropes and out on the cement floor headfirst. The mulatto was at the depot nervously waiting for the Denver train and wondering how it all came about before the club favorite could be revived.

For years in the late teens, a short, funny little man the writer only knew as "Muggins," had a popcorn wagon which he parked on the street at the Alliance National Bank corner. His product was nothing fancier than a generous drenching of butter on the exploded white kernels. Later Tom Cross, the high school janitor, purchased the wagon but had to move the business off the city street. He picked a location at the north end of the large outdoor sign board that screened the vacant lots of which the Fraternal Order of Eagles eventually built to accommodate the clubrooms upstairs and the L. B. Murphy store below. Old Tom raised two nephews, Les and Chuck, and probably acquired the popcorn wagon to keep them busy. They were popular kids in high school and the location was out of the wind, so it was a rendezvous for the high school crowd and a continual beckoning to the theatre-goer with the Imperial movie house only two buildings farther south.

One time in 1917, Chenia Newberry called Cy Laing, one time police chief but who at the time was testing different sandhill lakes with one Charley Howe for their potash content. Would he drop in at the store? Somebody was robbing the register till and Chenia thought it was an inside job. Would Cy hide out inside the store for a couple of nights if necessary and see if they could apprehend the pilferer? The answer was in affirmative and Cy let himself in the store shortly before dark. Soon after dark and before he had a chance to really hide, there was the turning of a key in the door and Byron Fosdick, one of the Newberry clerks, let himself in and made for the cash register. Cy had only time to step behind the big dapple grey mannequin of a horse used to demonstrate Newberry harness. (The same now greets a visitor at the Alliance Knight Museum in a display conceived as a 7th Cavalry mount by the late Jack Sampson.) As the pilferer was well into the cash drawer, Cy stepped out with "I'm awfully sorry this had to be you, Byron." Cy called Newberry who came right down to the store. After some little conference, it was decided that if Fosdick would join the army the next day there would be no charges filed. He did and there wasn't, but Fosdick was not heard of again, locally at least.

For a couple of years in about 1914 or 1915, Cy ran the Alliance Hotel Cafe and lived at 216 Toluca Avenue. The "boy" had a red coaster wagon and made that run between home and the cafe several times daily. Most of the distance called for coasting over a board walk, there was very little concrete at that time; but he was quite a coaster. The route was past Second and Cheyenne Avenue and "the house" of Silver Nell Thompson. This was a large two-story frame house with a screened-in porch on the front and one side. When the weather was nice, Nell and "the girls" aired five or six large green parrots by hanging their cages from the porch ceiling. They, the parrots, were a great attraction for the boy and he would stop and visit with them from the sidewalk. One day Cy received a call from Nell that went something like—"Mr. Laing, I hate to tell you this because Robert is such a nice little fellow, but he annoys our parrots as he goes by the house and teaches them naughty words. Please don't punish him but he really shouldn't do it anymore." Cy was not one to risk losing the nice business the cafe enjoyed when some of the sports would call for steak dinners to be sent over to 132 Cheyene. He stopped the parrot thing but not without administering some back-side punishment to that "nice little fellow."

Phillip Fortune was a middle-aged man, a tailor by profession, who came to Alliance from Chicago for health reasons. Mr. Fortune also played the bass violin with expertise. In the early twenties, Bill Edwards organized a "legitimate" orchestra made up of a surprising number of excellent musicians. The group was sort of sponsored by the Methodist Church so a short series of concerts was arranged. One night the audience was a full house, the orchestra members were all in place but there was no Phil Fortune. The wait was "full of silence" and very embarrassing. Suddenly there was a commotion at the front door as Phil came in. He had trouble getting his bass fiddle through a door that was not intended to accommodate a seven foot instrument but he eventually figured how to give a little at the top and bring it through bottom first. That was not the end of his scene, however. Phil had to try negotiating the middle aisle. Bang! Bang! That was too narrow so he tried the left or south aisle. It was no better but was louder if anything as the flushed but resolute man finally made it to the front, banging first a pew then the wall, the full distance. The decibels made by the case of the large instrument hitting against seats and then the wall was exceeded only by the termented aroma that permeated all areas near the man's path through the church. He finally completed his confused journey to his place in the orchestra stand and the program proceeded. All went well and an hour spent strumming and picking those heavy thick strings seemed to sober Phil considerably, but somehow he didn't play in the Methodist Church after that.

One would think that with all the natural difficulties encountered in the early days, that community leaders would get along peacefully in their unified efforts to build a town. According to the minutes of the Village Board in 1889 and 1890 this was not so. Town meetings moved around—sometimes they were held in the office of one of the trustees, more often in the office of the Village Clerk. F. M. Devore was village clerk and attorney in 1889 but wanted to retire. William Mitchell was appointed to the combined offices and, of course, as pointed out earlier in these pages, could not get along with others. Meetings were held for several months in his office. On February 5, 1890, the Board removed Mitchell from office. Several trustees in turn acted as clerk in a "pro tem" capacity. By April 8, 1890, when a new board took office, Mitchell had not and would not surrender the minutes and records from his office. A committee was appointed "to call on Wm. Mitchell and request that he turn over the records." The board adjourned to April 15 and Mr. Devore was reappointed Village Clerk and Attorney. In the May 16, 1890 meeting, the attorney was instructed "to get the records (from Mitchell's office) in the most expeditious way possible." Just what way that was is left unreported but there is a minute book, in continuity, in the city offices for the period. This may be more ludicrous and interesting to a former clerk than to the reader.

XVI. Conclusion

The now "seventy-two year old boy" stopped writting to muse a bit over the foregoing. The severe winter of 1979, starting with the minus 33 degrees below zero New Year's Eve, had helped to keep him from putting off the writing experience; organizing and typing the reminiscence helped to stave off the "cabin fever" to which he was exposed to for the next two months. He again has concluded that he has lived in a very unusual century, the Twentieth.

The advances might be summed up "to equal the square of the sum of all previous progress made by man since he started to walk upright, moved out of the cave and invented the wheel." For as he picked out each of the experiences covered in this narrative, he omitted dozens of closely allied sidelights.

What century can claim the infinite apex reached by so many advances and developments as can be observed, but not necessarily understood, as in the fields of nuclear energy, the airplane, computers, vaccine and other disease preventions, air conditioning, stratosphere exploring and space travel, surgery, generation and use of electricity, the automobile, fabrics and many, many, other things.

Now a little more about those omissions, it is better if man does not undertake the mastery of all things. If he obeys the old adage "to stop and smell the flowers as he goes along life's way," it is better that he concentrate on the fragrance of one posy but remember how it blended with the entire flower bed. From all of his maze of progress, let's take one subject, communication. A beneficent monopoly, which shall be unnamed, has improved the telephone and its service to a point where it is almost indispensable; the old music boxes, the Edison and the Victrola, have gone through the orthophonic and then the stereo stages; radio, first with earphones, crystal sets and speakers, had employed megacycles, kilocycles, FM and AM to perfect many private and public special applications; and then came television, first in black and white, then in color, tube and solid state. Now almost every home owns a combination of all — stereo for records or radio in AM or FM, solid state and color, the reception for which is taken directly from the atmosphere or is transmitted on a closed circuit from a central station with many channels available.

The overwhelming miracle of it all moves him to recall the following prayer for which we are indebted to "anonymous" and which has such universal applicability:

74

God, grant me the serenity to accept
The things I cannot change,
The courage to change the things I can
And the wisdom to know the difference.

* * * * *

VI

Like the "apology" ahead of LEGEND AND
MEMORY, PHASE II of LEGEND AND
MEMORY has been previously published as a
booklet (1980). It deals with further reminiscing by the writer on people and events past of
Alliance, Nebraska. We felt that it too should
be included in the SMORGASBORD.

Phase II of Legend and Memory

Characters

Cliff Robinson was a young pharmacist just out of school and fortunate enough to have been hired as a druggist in the Holsten drug store. In the short time he had been home, he was meeting the townspeople and was particularly popular with the young people. He was adept at putting names with faces, but shortly after eight o'clock one morning as he opened the store for business, he was to have a real test.

A young fellow, obviously breathless from running several blocks to get an errand accomplished before school, burst through the door, picked up three rolls of toilet paper, held them up for Cliff to see and started to leave with instructions, "just charge it." Cliff knew the kid's face, but for the life of him could not think of his name. He had to act quickly as Rex Thompson, youngest son of the city Mayor, was already up to the front of the store. "Who's that for?" he shouted, for he knew the boy belonged to a regular charging-customer family. Rex was out the front door, but he braked his exit enough to shout back over his shoulder, "All of us!" and was gone.

*　*　*　*　*

Ernest C. Miller was and is funny. Not in any sense in the "odd" sort of funny, for Ernie's observations are very complete and his conclusions mirror a keen grasp of all happenings. Comical would be a much better choice of word. He wasn't perfect of course, for he had permitted his 200 pound physique of baseball pitching days to boom up to 260 pounds, and he felt more at home swinging a number three or five wood off the tee instead of "busting one" down the fairway with a number one wood. However, with age, his wit became even sharper, quicker, and often more cryptic. When Ernie's eyes began to fail, he sold his accounting practice and had time on his hands. He was 65.

One day the writer, who had been retired for several years and took considerable kidding about it, entered the lounge at the golf course clubhouse and there was Ernie – hot, sweaty and tired from playing 18 holes; but with shoes off, reclining in an easy chair with stocking feet resting on another chair and a cold drink in his hand – the picture of relaxation. He had this greeting. "Say Roberts, I'm retired now. Am I doing it right?"

* * * * *

The fear of losing some time (it might be an hour, a day or a week) has often been manifest by the "old school type" of laborer, particularly in the days before unions, grievance committees and fringe benefits. Call it faithfulness to the job or to fear some lost wages, an incident in the Alliance power plant back in the early thirties, illustrates an extreme to which an elderly employee would go to escape the possible penalty of his mistake.

Bawly (L. L.) Wood was an employee in his upper sixties, who would have been retired by today's standards in personnel administration. He had been a fixture in the Alliance plant for years, but only as a maintenance man. Faithful and hardworking, he never quite made it as an operator and only on unusual occasions was he entrusted with the lesser skills expected of a fireman. Advanced technical requirements for operators and assistant plant operators (a more prestigious title for a fireman) would be required in the new plant, which the administration was planning and on which construction was commenced in 1938. Bawly's status never could be more than that of a maintenance man.

One afternoon, Carl Rockey the plant superintendent, entered the plant from out-of-doors and detected an odor, which he immediate-

1914 panorama of City of Alliance taken from second floor

ly thought of as burned flesh. There was no indication of excitement in the crew, or apparent trouble with the equipment—the turbine was "purring" smoothly. So Rockey asked no questions, but made a swing around through the plant looking for an explanation of that unusual stench, which became less noticeable as it blended with the smell of coal dust and steam. He finally came upon Bawly doing some cleanup chore, but wearing a glove on one hand, which was very unusual for Bawly.

"Bawly, what's the matter with your hand?" Rockey demanded. "Oh nothing," was Wood's reply, "just a little burn." "Let me see that paw!" Rockey was now a little irritated with the evasiveness of the older man. "Take off that glove," he said sharply. "It never got through the callous" defended Bawly, but he began removing the grimy glove. Rockey had to help him part the flannel sticking to the ooze of cooked flesh, took him to the doctor at once and probably headed off a serious infection from the burn caused by Bawly grabbing hold of a hot steam pipe—even though "it never got through the callous" of that gnarled old hand, hardened by a lifetime of work.

* * * * *

When the curtain fell, in 1966, upon the life of Hayes Chandler, it was as though a solid pillar of the community had been removed. The plain, honest, unsophisticated everyday living routine of this black man, upon whom so many had depended upon to perform menial tasks, who had brightened the lives of so many children, as gone. His very appearance had commanded attention. Strangers almost always gave him an appraising look and at once catalogued him as definitely a member of "the old school."

window of Old High School looking south.

Hayes Chandler (1882-1966)

Hayes was 22 years of age when he and his wife Florence came from Mississippi to Box Butte County and settled on a farm near Hemingford. Later he moved the family to Alliance and soon became the town's handyman. From the Chandler home in Hills Addition, in the southwest and "across-the-track" section of the city, he operated a dray-like business with a light weight, antique wagon, possessed of the loudest iron rims on its wooden spoked wheels, when traveling the paved streets. The wagon was pulled by a team, which like its master, never seemed to age. They had already reached the age plateau where haste was no longer a virtue, nor was it expected of them. That made for a mutual understanding with the man that fed them and was tolerant and unhurried about the world's pace as they.

Nothing heightened a child's birthday party like a ride in that rickety old wagon; and no Presidential guard was more attentive than the old gentleman with a sharp eye on the safety of those gleeful and happy kids who piled aboard for a scheduled ride "with Hayes."

All rides were not by prior arrangement. Hayes was a "pied Piper" for children. With the wagon empty, he would usually stop to accommodate kids, who would run out into the street to board that old wagon for a couple of blocks of sheer pleasure. On one occasion, Tommy Laing ran out behind the rig while it was moving, and attempted to board it unobserved. Climbing onto the wagon box, Tommy slipped and fell under the rear wheel. Only then did Hayes realize that he (almost) had a passenger. He stopped the team with a loud "Whoa" and was off the seat with a nimble display of agility to assist the almost certain-to-be injured boy. Fortunately, the wagon was empty and although the wheel passed over Tommy's backside and hip, there were no broken bones or other serious injury. Tommy scrambled up, realized he was okay and then ran for home, scared of the entire incident. It had all happened so quickly. Several neighbors were witness to the incident. All shared relief that the boy was not badly hurt and were equally happy for Hayes, who though faultless in the matter, would have suffered the agony of self-blame had it been otherwise.

One tragic incident occuring in the saga of Hayes Chandler, came in the form of a bad fire which literally burned him out of the ways he made his living – horses, wagon and all went up in flames with the barn. A fund for his relief was immediately established and contributions were many. The most notable and unusual was that made by Jack Resigeau, head of the Alliance Livestock Sales Ring. It was a new team and wagon, complete with harness and tack and lacking only in one respect – with rubber tires, gone would be the metalic clanging of the old metal wheels that announced Hayes Chandler's presence up and down Alliance streets.

The lovable old character, had he lived another fifteen years, would have enjoyed the maturing and successes of the Chandler children and grandchildren. Hayes Jr., a son and the oldest, lives in Alliance, is employed by Neuswangers, has served his country and emulates the happy, likeable personality of the father. Orkritta, the second child, married Forrest Shores of another well-known local family and lives in Colorado. Then came twin daughters, Maude McGuire, who is married and lives in Indianapolis, Indiana. She mothered Myrtle Chandler, who only recently was appointed Director of the Box Butte County welfare office; and Myrtle Nickens, deceased but who mothered from very modest beginnings, an unusual family of six. LeRoy, the second son, and Danny live in Alliance and work for the railroad; Ernie Jr. lives in Wichita and is a chemist with the Vulcan Chemical Company of that city; Betty is a claim agent for Mutual of Omaha insurance company, Johnny, the youngest, is at this time, a senior in Kearney State College majoring in French and English and with a yen to become a writer; Florence Nickens, to whom I am indebted for much of this story is a Manpower Specialist with CETA, Cooperative Education Training Act, administered by and with the Nebraska Employment Office in Alliance.

Truly, the parental influence of Hayes and Florence Chandler is very apparent.

* * * * *

Just Narrating

Bill Zieg has painted a lot of signs, hunted a lot of rocks, polished a lot of agates and told a lot of stories in his time. One of his best deals with an incident in the early 20th century.

At the time, the Zieg family lived in Crawford, Nebraska, where Bill's dad was the town marshal. A company of colored troops was quartered at nearby Fort Robinson. When a white girl was assaulted and raped, one of the blacks was taken into custody. Feeling ran high in the town gaining particular momentum for a lynching in a local saloon. Marshal Zieg had a responsibility to protect his prisoner so when the spirit of the mob reached a peak, he left his office and jail via the back door with the prisoner, going to his home to pick up a second mount for the black man; and also to say goodbye to Mrs. Zieg, who was "heavy with child." The two men escaped the mob by the narrowest of margins.

The mob arrived at the Zieg home in a nasty, impatient mood and it took a little time for Mrs. Zieg to convince its spokesman, who had to look inside the house, that there was no one else home. A couple of days later, the Marshal reached Chadron, where his charge was jailed and he could hurry back home to his wife.

Looking back, Bill recalls, "That scene provided by the angry mob was very scary for my mother," then pausing for the full effect of the listener, he added, "That night I was born, May 18, 1906."

Note: The writer felt obligated to check the foregoing story with Bill for verification and permission to use it. He asked Bill if he had any suggestions to make. Bill replied, "Yes if you want to use it. The night Dad left with the prisoner, Art Moss, his deputy, was shot to death. It was generally conceded that Deputy Moss was mistaken for Marshal Zieg."

* * * * *

One of the most looked-forward-to annual experience used to be the opening every spring of Bauman's cabin, near Sheridan Lake in the Black Hills. Doctor "B. G." scheduled this outing under the pretense of cleaning up the cabin and making it suitable as his mother's summer residence in which she entertained a number of friends, usually playing bridge. To the best of my memory, very little was ever done by members of B. G.'s guest list towards putting that cabin in any shape that would meet the niceties required by

Mother Bauman. Oh of course, we turned the water on after it had been laid to rest for the winter. We always had a load of wood hauled in and split most of it to kindling size and sometimes we washed the pans and dishes; but dusting, sweeping, mopping and washing the windows – somehow the start on those little chores never survived the poker game or a fishing turn on Sheridan Lake. I'm sure that Leona, Doc's mother, must have had an excellent rapport with some "domestic" in the Hill City community for such "woman's work."

William (Bill) Roberts, a former Burlington engineer and my uncle, had retired to a few acres he acquired a couple of miles south of Hill City. He called it Soda Gulch. That Roberts name indicates that he must share some guilt with my mother for that s on the end of my given name. Well, he paid for that guilt partially by carrying throughout his life the nickname of "Beany." My uncle was somewhat of a character so it was little wonder that upon meeting him, the fascination of "Soda Gulch" and "Uncle Beany" was a little heady for Bauman's guests.

Another Allianceite, who had a cabin in the hills, was James Hunter. By Jim's invitation, a bunch of us were to spend an evening with him and Dr. O. L. Seng, his house guest. Bauman's "Do Drop Inn" was northeast of Hill City, Hunter's was southeast. Soda Gulch lay midway between the two.

The little visit commenced while there was still daylight. Departure from the Hunter cabin was near midnight. Jim's hospitality had been generous and as we neared the hiway, someone suggested that we should visit Uncle Beany. Everyone was for that. As the driver, I could hardly veto the clamorous suggestion; as a relative, I was a little apprehensive about the hour and condition of my friends.

There was a light in the kitchen of the house at Soda Gulch, so we turned in and knocked noisily. The door was opened by Aunt Betty. She and her three woman friends were sitting around the table chit chatting. Two of those women were visitors from the east but obviously had come ability, and luck, as fisherwomen, for before we could ask the whereabouts of Uncle Beany, one of them arose and brought from the refrigerator a nice seven pound rainbow trout, still with its beautiful markings and definitely a trophy fish. It was part of her catch for the day and after being mounted, would have a future above the fireplace back home.

It wasn't long before Uncle Beany appeared in the bedroom doorway to see what all the fuss was about. He had been sound asleep and in another bedroom, "Red" Austin, of the T. V. movie *Orphan Train* was asleep and "dead to the world." He had a turn running the 1880 train in the morning, and when we all paraded into his bedroom to pay our respects, his response was a little less than enthusiastic. Anyhow, after another "nightcap" with Uncle Beany and "the girls" we paid our respect to that fine fish and left for Baumans. We had early morning fishing on the lake in our program.

It was between 10:00 and 11:00 a.m. when we called the fishing a day with various degrees of luck. As we entered the driveway of the cabin, there was Uncle Beany. He knew who had wood for sale so B. G. had asked him to bring out a load sometime. He hardly expected such promptness. Later as B. G. and I were alone with him, Beany explained, "I wouldn't come back over there for a couple of days—until those two women had left." It seems that when everyone there got up in the morning, there was that beautiful trout laying on the kitchen table. No one had thought to return it to the freezer.

Why aren't those outings continued today? Well, B. G.'s father had built that cabin on government leased land. There was a very plain stipulation in the lease that it could be reclaimed at any time with proper notice and was all fair and right because the government wanted to extend and include the site in a wilderness area. Who could conceive Baumans without a cabin? Subsequently, B. G., together with Drs. Taylor, Morgan and Kennedy, built a new cabin about a mile upstream, after purchasing its site outright. It was modern to the nth degree—so the wives would have a little more enthusiasm for it, but the Bauman cabin trips were never quite the same after that.

* * * * *

Alliance Country Club, circa 1925

I never play number ten fairway on Alliance Skyview golf course and pass the three evergreens grouped just outside the south fairway line and about 135 years from the green, but I'm reminded of how they happened to be there.

As City Manager, I had scheduled the removal of those particular trees from the South Park, where they were growing bigger and bigger and were a definite traffic hazard at the intersection of Potash and First Streets. The city had two men, handy as rough carpenters, cement workers, et cetera, that were shuffled around in several departments. This day they were assigned to the park and the golf course. During the forenoon, Charley Woods and Al Boness dug three holes for the trees at the course and then dug out the trees, the roots of which they "balled" to perfection, retaining within the burlap wrapping as much of the natural dirt as possible. (The city had not yet acquired that hallowed piece of equipment—a tree spade.)

Charley and Al were past masters at planning a day's work and so arrived at the golf course with the trees loaded on a truck just a comfortable hour before quitting time. They carefully unloaded the first tree and lowered it into the awaiting hole and tamped it in carefully. Charlie Hitt, a retired railroader, and one of the course's regulars, was just coming down the fairway but stopped about 40 yards away to watch the operation. The second tree was set with equal dispatch. Hitt was really impressed. Then came the third three. For some reason, perhaps one of the men looked at his watch and was concerned that they might not get back into town in time to quit for the day, but that third tree toppled off the end gate of the truck and the ball of dirt around its roots disintegrated from the weight and force of the fall. Boness said, "Laing sure will raise hell with us now!" Woods said, "Get the damned thing into the hole and covered. They ain't going to live anyhow." Charlie Hitt could hardly wait until the next morning to report it to me. He was my first "customer" and was convulsed with his joke while telling it.

Well, time flies and is also a great healer. There are no three trees on the entire golf course today (some 18 years later) that are anywhere near as healthy as those three evergreens.

* * * * *

One night at the bar of the Alliance Country Club, a stranger, attempting to make small talk with the bartender, Rusty Albright, pointed at Doc Kosmicki being seated at one of the dining room tables, asked, "Do you know the Kosmickis?" "Hell yes," replied Rusty,

"Everyone knows the Kosmickis. There's only one tribe bigger, that's the Sioux.

Truly an interesting family, or clan, in the community of Alliance and Box Butte County, has been the Kosmickis. They are not "old timers" in terms of being early settlers. T. B. (Toefil Barnard) and Tom were two of a family of thirteen children born to Lawrence and Rose in Lamont, Illinois, (there is a difference of opinion among T. B.'s offspring – some insisting that it was Cicero instead of Lamont) that ended up in Sioux County and Box Butte County after Poland-born Lawrence, T. B.'s father had moved the family from Illinois to Sherman County (Loup City) Nebraska in 1882.

Another family living in the neighborhood (Ashton) was that of Ed Zochol. There follows an interesting succession of intermarriage between the two families. Teofil Kosmicki married Martha Zochol; Tom Kosmicki married Theresa Zochol; Adam Kosmicki married Frances Zochol and Frank Zochol married Mary Kosmicki.

The T. B. and Tom Kosmickis and Ed Zochols arrived in Hemingford, Nebraska in the spring of 1913 on an immigrant train. They had one freight car per family for their entire possessions – tools, furniture, farm equipment and livestock. T. B. located on a homestead in Sioux County, Tom worked as a day laborer before farming and Zochol homesteaded near Hemingford before moving to a farm northeast of Alliance. As the writer is far more familiar with the family of Teofil, except with reference to Tom and his son Raymond, this story will be mainly concerned with T. B. and the Kosmickis of Box Butte County.

In 1916 and 1918, T. B. moved to farms nearer Hemingford and later, about 1925 to the Riley farm northeast of Alliance, where Leonard lives today. Then later, he moved to the big, square, white house twelve miles north of Alliance on U.S. 385. Individuals of three generations since have furnished color in sports, have been exemplary in dry land wheat farming, and to the man, or woman, have been vocal and extremely capable of terse, poignant to-the-point observations on almost any subject of local or world interest.

Baseball and golf were the main organized sports engaged in, although Mike, Bob and Bill were top athletes in high school football and basketball. Bob and Bill formed a formidable battery for American Legion Junior baseball and were mainstays in the line for St. Agnes Academy football teams. Mike played both football and basketball for Alliance High School and was an outstanding pitcher for the Legion teams with the result he was scouted and signed by the St. Louis Cardinals in professional baseball. After two years with Cardinal farm teams at Dothan, Alabama and St. Petersburg, Florida, he was released from pro ball and turned his talent in sports to golf. He has always been a tournament contender passing a good deal of talent onto his son Kurt. Both, along with Tom and Jim, of Raymond's family, will always be counted in among the low handicap players.

In spite of the family prolificacy, the genetic lines were strong and sound in producing many healthy, young and aggressive males. The "Kosmicki Kids" made little or no trouble in the community. In those twenties and thirties while growing up, the brothers, and cousins, banded together at Saturday night dances and other occasions. In those days of "the great experiment" prohibition, troublemakers seeking to violate the law and looking for low cost entertainment necessitated by the Great Depression, thought twice before provoking any trouble with the Kosmicki boys.

Generally, if there was any spunk left after long hours of farm work, excess energy was worked off with a baseball. There were many rural community hard ball teams such as Snake Creek, Fairview, Berea and . . . the Kosmickis. By the mid thirties, their collective talent and energy had been funneled into softball in town. It had become a craze, enjoying better diamonds and even a lighted field. Night games were a tremendous advantage for players and spectators alike. Alliance boasted a "hot" eight team league for several years.

Deeply involved at the height of this softball hysteria were the Kosmickis. There were not quite enough brothers to comprise a team, but there were cousins. Their team was sponsored by a local oil company. Another team, sponsored by the *Times-Herald* semi-weekly newspaper, was organized and coached by one Harry Ukulele, a Hawaiian swimming and basketball transplant, who claimed a sports editor title with the paper and supplemented that living with various officiating jobs. Uke was a star in any sport.

The season one year ended with the Kosmickis (Texaco) tied with the *Times-Herald*. A three game playoff was arranged and held with the Kosmickis outfit an odds on favorite over the bunch of young neophites coached and held together by the Hawaiian magician. After the first two games each team claimed a win. The Texaco team, after clowning around in its one loss, should have won the third game, the playoff, had it not concentrated so heavily on hitting to and ribbing a substitute third baseman, who handled every offering without error.

Dryland farming in Box Butte County was certainly a marginal operation prior to the Henry Wallace-Franklin Roosevelt agriculture program. Bean and corn crops made a sad picture at harvest time with the short season between frosts and, then there was the added spector of drought and the dust bowl. The Kosmickis stuck with wheat farming. They complied with federal recommended practices, which in view of marketing restrictions imposed for non-compliance, were almost mandatory.

They summer fallowed, strip farmed, managed acreage allotments and acquired more land. While no one man could be classed as "the biggest wheat farmer" collectively, the Kosmickis would have to be considered among the high producers in the county. Even today, there is only one irrigation well on Kosmicki land, and that is on Paul's, the Alliance Postmaster.

In spite of hail and other natural losses in the high-risk occupation of farming, several of those dry land wheat farmers (including the family mentioned) are usually able to have their risks and efforts rewarded with off-season pleasures – some trips to Las Vegas and the like. The writer is not sure which operation makes the other possible, but knowing the Kosmickis, it is probably a combination of both hard work and hard play.

Grandparents	Their children & spouse	Grandchildren & spouse	Number of Great Grandchildren
T.B. Teofil Kosmicki, married Martha Zochol	Floyd (Slim) married Ella Matz	Mary Jo, Fred Koehnke	5
		Marg, Ev Dietlein	3
		Martha, Phillip Morris	1
	Marion (Buck) married Margaret Bicknell	Mike, Sandra Brockway	3
		Pat, Eleanor Parker	2
		Tim	
	Leonard (Bill) married Lillian Van Velson	Nick, Kay McCarthy	2
		George, Dixie Becker	3
		Helen, P. McCarthy, then J. Berry	2 & 3
		John, Rene Thompson	1
	Donald (Doc) married Blance Moore	Karen, Willard Dietrich	2
		Bill, 2nd marriage, Dillon	3
		Bob, 2nd marriage, Ann Morton	1
	Paul (Sandy) married Mildred Munger	Mary Letha, unmarried	
		Mark, deceased	
		Cynthia, Fred Kimmel	4
		Gregg, Debbie Penn	1
		Denice, unmarried	
		Theron, Unmarried	
		Dannielle, M. Koetteman	1
		Elise, unmarried	
	John (Jeep) married Pauline Stec	Steve, unmarried	
		Dave, Theresa	
		Theodore, unmarried	
		Edward	
		Marty	
		Mathew	
		Je	
		James	
Tom Kosmicki married Theresa Zochol	Raymond married Margie McCullaugh	Marelene, Les Reno	3
		Tom, Theresa Z.	
		Jim (Shep)	
		Catherine	
		Theresa	
		Laura	
		Angela	
	Martin		
	Pricilla		
	Marie		
	Dorothy (deceased)		
	Clementine (deceased)		
	Ellen Ann		

The above is as the writer knew or was aware of late in the year of 1979.

Snow Geese milling around City Water Tank.

In a discussion of federal regulations on wildlife to save certain endangered species of migratory waterfowl (the whooping crane in this instance) that an official of the State Game Commission attempted to explain why Nebraska did not have an open season on the sandhill crane. It comes through central Nebraska in the spring of the year in great numbers. The birds swarm the Platte River and other waters in great numbers and perform such antics that the natives await their arrival and the state newspapers carry items and pictures of them. In the autumn, the birds apparently take a different route south to their wintering grounds. During the Nebraska hunting season, there just aren't enough birds to justify an open season. This is odd because other states the south enjoy an open season on sandhill cranes. This is similar to the morning dove. Only recently has our state had a dove season although many of these birds are hatched and matured in Nebraska.

Behavior of our migrators has always fascinated me. For instance, every March 1, I begin to watch for the snow geese. Every spring there will be between five and ten thousand of those beautiful, noisy birds congregated about fifteen miles northeast of Alliance. They spend one, two, sometimes three weeks in the neighborhood before continuing their long flight north. There is a statewide limit on snow geese in the fall. Hunters along the Missouri River seem to have a dependable flight of these birds, but in the panhandle, a single, noisy gaggle of "snows" might be all that the regular hunter would see, or hear, all season.

In the spring the great flocks make a beautiful spectacle against a clear, blue sky. It is not unusual for them to fly low over town at night, become confused and lost in the reflections of the street lights milling back and forth for hours.

Funny? Not So Funny

An invitation to dinner in the private car of a Burlington Railroad official was an occasion to remember. As City Manager and in charge of the municipal power plant which burned coal, I was on occasion included as a guest. The railroad always was interested in "the haul" of all that coal from the Wyoming mines. Others included in the guest list were in local finance, the newspaper, grain elevators and areas developing heavy freight. The event was a gesture of appreciation to keep smooth the status quo, since delivery of our coal requirements was quite remote for carriers other than the railroad. In the days prior to the big stock trucks taking over the movement of livestock, there was always a representative of the sales ring invited. That practice was terminated as the trucks won out over the railroads.

On this occasion the guest list included Ben J. Sallows, publisher; Chris and LeRoy Abbot and Fred Harris, bankers; George Neuswanger, grain elevator and three prominent ranch owners — Monahan, Manning and Henderson. Dinner started with a highball and some tasty hors d'oeuvers, after which we were ushered into the dining section of the car, which was resplendent with white linens, sparkling glassware and generous settings of heavy silverware and fine china. Three capable black waiters were immaculate in their starched, white jackets. One of them was an acquaintance and while he nodded courteously, I could read his thought, "What de hell yo' all doin' here Laing?"

First came a relish dish on which we placed whatever fruit we wished from a heaping dish offered by a waiter. Then came a hot soup course, which was most appetizing. Then the main entree came, which almost caused me to choke. We had three large raisers of beef and others with cattle interests at the table, and those waiters were setting before them the biggest, thickest lamb chop I had ever seen. It was browned to perfection and looked like a roast. I don't suppose there were fifty sheep within a fifty mile radius of us, but I thought, here was our host insulting those cattlemen by serving lamb.

Well, I was very naive and wrong in my thinking. Every plate was cleaned voraciously. The table then was cleared quickly of nonessentials and readied for a non-filling dessert, an ice cream type served with hot coffee. One of the waiters then passed a box of fresh, fragrant corona cigars. Some were not finished eating but the others lit up and when the slower eaters finished, we all retired to the parlor section of the car and settled back to visit.

I felt very fortunate and relaxing back in my chair, bountifully fed and most graciously hosted – I wasn't mad at anybody. But, the thought continued to cross my mind – why lamb to entertain cattlemen? Guess I'd just read too many stories about early day range wars between the sheepmen and cattlemen.

* * * * *

Oley Saylor and I were golfing buddies of long standing. One time I was to pick him up quite early for breakfast and then a day of golf. I expected him to be half asleep, so sounded the horn a couple to times before he sort of stumbled out of the back door of the duplex, where he lived, and entered the garage. It occurred to me that he had left something in his car that he needed and then "bang!" Out of that garage came Oley, car and all, without ever opening the garage door – no further comment.

* * * * *

Charles (Chuck) O'Bannon was a personable fellow with a Jekyll and Hyde characteristic that often cropped out in his checkered career as a farmer and in many avenues of mischief-making as a man-about-town. His was the cherub face and persuasive personality that accounted for some non-resident friends and connections. This was particularly true during the hunting season. Chuck was an excellent shot and inveterate hunter. The fact that he was one of the county's biggest trespassers when hunting, while his own land was posted solidly with no hunting signs, meant nothing to him. The Omaha and Chicago bankers, and others, usually wealthy people, to whom he would furnish guide service, were either unaware of his idiosyncracies or didn't care as long as he put them onto the game and sent them home with their bag limits filled.

My Street Superintendent, Fred Schlothauer, was a buddy of O'Bannon. This worried me some, but he was never in trouble or connected with any of Chuck's escapades. Fred's great weakness was his gluttony. On this occasion, he was invited to a stag party at the O'Bannon home. Chuck was divorced and his mother was out-of-town. One of those successful hunts was being celebrated with his guests (or customers) from the east. Among them was one man that really could play the piano. Fred was fascinated with the fellow and when not helping O'Bannon with the hospitality duties, he was seated beside the pianist, suggesting tunes and enjoying himself immensely.

Finally Chuck refreshed the music maker's glass and said, "Last drink. The ducks are about ready to eat." "Just a half of one for me," said the guest. "Nobody can eat a whole mallard." Chuck looked at him askance and said, "Hell, this man sitting beside you can eat three!" That was beyond belief, and out of the friendly argument that developed a twenty dollar wager was made that Schlothauer could not eat three mallard ducks with all the "fixin's." Fred wondered too, but he felt he had to protect and win his host's wager. He did, but the rest of that night and all next day, he was one sick Dutchman.

* * * * *

Krause's "home lake" was a wild duck mecca, and one day in the fall of 1922, Ed Yarter, a high school friend, and I made a killing, filling our limits with mallards. I was quite taken with the old model '97 Winchester hammer gun that Ed was using. After trying it out, we agreed on a trade for a second gun of mine, which was at home. We had met on the lake, so each had his own car and so went home our separate ways.

When I arrived home, I could hardly wait to pick up the traded gun and deliver it to Ed in exchange for his. Then home in the front room, I very foolishly slipped a half dozen shells in the magazine and pumped them out. I have never figured out what happened, but with the third shell, the gun discharged and blew a large hole through the wall. I was petrified and took the gun out in the back yard to eject the rest of the shells, which it did without fault. I used the gun for several years after that without it ever repeating that misfiring.

Back in the house, I took inventory of the damage. How fortunate could I be that no one else was home? The charge of shot, powder and wadding had blown a ten inch hole through the wall and what a mess it had made of the pillows and the bed, where my sister Betty slept, just beyond that wall!

Incidents of Note

It has never been hard for me to recall within a few day's accuracy, Dr. F. P. Sucgang's locating in Alliance. The good Doctor came to Alliance from Kimball, Nebraska area late in October, 1931. His life at that time had included a jump from his native Philippines and the adjustment of that move with enrollment at the University of Nebraska, and later, with studies in Austria in the field of his specialties — eye, ear, nose and throat.

One could hardly fault him for making the change. That community was demanding of him to assume the responsibilities of a general practice, rather than the pursuit of a practice for which he had been trained. The term "cash flow" was not then in common use, but had it been, the Doctor would have been the first to acknowledge that his cash flow was practically zero. Accepting payment of his fee for a maternity case in so many chickens, and in one instance, he became the owner of a milk cow in settlement of an account, common practice in those early thirties, but not one that the Doctor could endure for long.

He picked Alliance because it appeared progressive, had a steady railroad and creamery payroll; and perhaps, the two surfaced tennis courts in the city park promised pursuit of his favorite sport at that time. He made the move with a modicum of equipment, rented some office space, paid for a month's board and room at Rose Krejci's room and boarding house, transferred his very modest bank account to the town's largest bank and hurried off to a professional meeting in Omaha.

The next morning, in Omaha, he read the large headlines in the *Omaha Bee-News* newspaper, "Largest Alliance Bank Closes Doors." Can anyone fully appreciate the frustration of our newest resident at that time?

* * * * *

Cy Laing, Police Chief, and Matt Berg, Burlington Special Agent and later County Sheriff, were close in both their work and friendship, but were quite competitive in their gardening — each thought that his was the "greenest thumb."

One time Cy was picking up "the makings" for prisoner's meals in a local grocery store, as was the routine for jail feeding in those days, when he noticed on display, the first "home-grown" tomatoes.

Cy Laing, Police Chief

Matt Berg, Sheriff

They were nice – easily recognized and distinguished from the smooth, pale, waxed and tasteless hothouse tomatoes offered throughout the spring and winter seasons. Cy bought a half dozen of them and dropped them off at the Berg home when he went to lunch, charging Mrs. Berg with telling Matt that "Cy had dropped by and left some nice tomatoes, the first from his garden." Of course, without a hothouse, this was ridiculous. Matt's tomato vines were as advanced as any local – a few "green marbles" just emerging from the blossoms testified to that. Never-the-less, while Laings were eating lunch, some-one asked, "What is Matt Berg doing out in our alley?"

Matt was inspecting Cy's tomato patch. Cy was convulsed with laughter. His prank was rewarded beyond expectation.

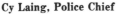

Whenever Scotty Henderson, an early day Sioux County rancher, came to town, the trip was not complete without a visit with long-time friend, Dr. F. M. Knight, president of the Alliance National Bank.

If Doc had a customer in his office, it made little difference to the little Scotchman. He would barge right in, station himself at the window and nervously tap his foot until the conference was concluded. No one else would have dreamed of such trespassing on the Doctor's time – except Scotty, after he had spent a little time at another port-of-call like Simon Spry's Saloon next door. Such in-trusion was not always the case, but it happened and Doc tolerated it.

Usually, the visit was of a more leisure pattern. When Doc's have-a-chair invitation was accepted by Scotty, both men, after exchanging cordialities, would swing their chairs around to and facing the window and watch the "goings on" at the interesection of Third Streeet and Box Butte Avenue. Each man might be deep in his own thoughts but each had great respect for the other. The silence was "deafening" and more than once a teller would find occasion to peer through the open door of the office just to see if, with the lack of conversation, everything was all right.

Outside the street, traffic was moving and Saturday shoppers made for an animated picture, quite different than both men remembered of an earlier days' calm on the dusty, unpaved streets with few pedestrians and no automobiles. Finally, one of the men (it might have been either) would say, "Look at it. Who would have believed it?" To which the other would answer in the affirmative. Both were living in the past at that moment and the expression by one mirrored the recall and reminiscence of the other of the sleepy, slow moving small town atmosphere of an earlier day.

Suddenly Doctor Knight would, with great feeling and depth of expression, recite a passage from one of Shakespeare's classics; to this Scotty might counter with an appropriate verse from Bobby Burns. Then both would laugh at such a strange application of literature to the urban scene. Doctor Knight, in his youth, had been a devout reader of Shakespeare with participation in the drama that entailed memorization; no one ever figured out where Scotty picked up his literary expertise, but he kept right up with the Doctor, when a passage from Bobby Burns or Robert Service was apropos.

Depth of the friendship that developed out of such camaraderie between the two men was demonstrated in October, 1931. For weeks there had been ominous things going on in Alliance business circles. A vicious run was developing on the First National Bank. It was the largest of the then three local banks and in those precarious days, it was financing more than its share of the farm and railroad community. Several days before it actually closed on October, 31, 1931, Scotty Henderson made one of his appearances at Doctor Knight's office. He closed the door behind him and placed himself close to the Doctor with an air that indicated he expected answers.

"What's going on across the street?" he asked, for the whispering about the doomed bank had circulated out of the county and into his neighborhood. The Doctor said, "Well Scotty, they are having a little trouble." "Really hurting?" asked Scotty. "Yes, I'm afraid so," was the reply. "Is it hurting you here?" Scotty pursued. "Oh, we have had some evidence of people's uneasiness with the situation, but nothing we cannot handle," the Doctor answered. "Listen Doc," said Scotty, "I want you to do this. You know what lands we own (forty sections or thereabouts) I want you to draw up a mortgage

100

on all—all of it. I'll sign it. Jennie will sign it. Then you take it to Omaha, Denver, or wherever you see fit. Discount it and get some money here on the spot. By God, they ain't going to do that to us!"

Doctor Knight said, "Thanks Scotty," but of course he never had to accept that most sincere and unsolicited offer of his friend.

* * * * *

One of the most confusing remarks that I ever heard was made by LeRoy Abbott one nice autumn afternoon in 1938. He excused himself from some meeting by saying, "Gee, I can't go tonight. Harry (Minor) and I have to go up and watch Uncle Matt (Minor) play football." Everyone laughed that two adults in their forties could have a seventeen year old uncle playing football for Alliance High School. I'll attempt an explanation at the risk of thoroughly confusing the reader.

It seems that Grandfather Minor had three families. The first family was blessed with Hannah (LeRoy's mother) and Joe Minor (Harry's father). That of course made LeRoy and Harry first cousins. Just to further confuse, the father of George Forbes, a banker in Laramie, Wyoming, married Hannah's and Joe's sister Ann, making George Forbes also a cousin of LeRoy and Harry. The grandfather's second family and three younger brothers of his first family migrated and located in Canada. Except as that branch, the Canadian Minors, visited several times with their Nebraska panhandle cousins and other relatives, not too many local people had made their acquaintance or were even aware of them.

Grandfather Minor's third marriage was to a southern woman and of course occurred much later. Their children included Matt, who was to live with Joe during his high school years. So there is the explanation of why two prominent Alliance men had set aside a Friday night to watch their seventeen year old uncle play football. Confusing? On the following page, we have attempted a more graphic explanation.

The foregoing also confirms the good advice that Harry Minor gave Dr. A. L. Goding one time, when as one of Doc's first patients and from his dentist chair advised him, "to never gossip, talk about or speak disparagingly of anyone from the sandhills—you might be talking to a relative."

* * * * *

Theodore Henry Minor, 1845-1932
and first wife
Mary Jane Hunter

Children

Anna (Mrs. George Forbes)

Joe Minor
Harry (Neva)
(Adopted Dick and Gloria)
Took Matt and Betty after
Joe died. Betty then adopted
by sister of Joe Miner's
second wife.
Edyth Snider
Mrs. Clark Jeary
Helen Farrar

Hannah Abbott Christopher
Arthur
Gladith
Phyllis
Jimmy (deceased, age 5)

Dode
John
Harry

Theodore Henry Minor
and second wife
Carrie Gaunt

Children

Hazel
Ike
David
Jim

Arthur (died young)
Dorothy Petersen
(Cathie and Shirley)
LeRoy
(LeRoy and James E.)

Theodore Henry Minor
and third wife
Maggie

Children

Rosie
Unnamed daughter
Sam (lived in Canada)
Matt (married Helen Johnson)
lives in Montana
Betty (lives in Honolulu)

These three brothers located in Canada and along with Sam, became better known as the "Canadian Uncles."
In 1927, Hannah, Joe and Arthur went to Mississippi to help the sick father
(Theodore) and Maggie. Rosie died. Theodore died in 1932. With Maggie
sick, Sam was sent to the Canadian uncles, Matt and Betty to Joe Minor.
Betty was subsequently adopted by Lottie, a sister of Joe's second wife.

Runways of Alliance Air Support Glider Base with Sky View Golf Course superimposed over the cantonment area. Buildings show up in black, the white objects are cement slabs from which barracks have been removed.

When the Alliance Air Support Glider Base was constructed in 1942-43, there was considerable engineering necessary considering that the site was on relatively flat terrain. Provision for drainage had to be made and the fill for miles of streets and runways accomplished. At one time twenty-three large earth movers (turn-a-pulls) were counted working feverishly building up roadbeds and bases for the four runways and huge apron. Utilities, such as electric, water and sewer systems, railroad yards to the large warehouse area, the bituminous surfacing of the many streets serving more than 600 buildings in the cantonment area were worked up and supervised by the Missouri River Engineers. Rush, rush, rush was the order each day. Supervision and keeping ahead of more than a dozen principal contractors, who were constantly pushing for attention in order to fulfill their building obligations, was no small assignment.

Finished layout maps of the base contained some unusual street names that would be hard to duplicate. The avenues A, B, C and the like were simple. Then there was Walker Avenue (Named after Col. D. Arthur Walker, a commanding officer), a Duck Avenue (because there were thousands of the migrators nesting in the near-by sandhills), there was a Loon Lane, but the name that caught my eye on the map was SNAFU Street. Some hard working and harried engineer was responsible for that one and explained its meaning – SITUATION NORMAL, ALL FOULED UP!

* * * * *

The 1904 nursing class of the Presbyterian Hospital in Chicago, which had also trained at the West Side Hospital of that city included the name of one Mary E. Roberts. She returned to her home in Springfield, Nebraska, without her diploma, because she had a job waiting for her in the Springfield hospital and then, she had stars in her eyes for a big, rawboned farm boy, by name of Cyrus Alexander Laing. In time they were married, but Cy had been adamant about setting of any wedding date other than, "just as soon as the corn gets laid by." "Laid by" is the term used in farming for the last cultivation before the crop gets too high to work it. Most brides are able to command a more definite wedding date, which in this case turned out to be July 13, so there was no big difference of opinion. However, Mary just "never got around" to taking the Nebraska examinations to be a Registered Nurse. That was to come much later.

The couple then moved to Alliance, where Mary found an abundance of work in private duty nursing and in assisting doctors, who apparently recognized her qualifications. That life pattern was interrupted in 1907 with the birth of the first-born son. Several years went by before there were any more children. Mary again was nursing. Her long suit was taking expectant mothers into her home, where they were cared for and the new baby ultimately delivered.

A 24 bed hospital was started in 1911, but it was 1916 before the first addition to the original St. Joseph Hospital was built. During that span of years, Mary Laing had all the practical nursing she could handle and yet give time to her family. After the children attained ages that gave her some "escape time," she gradually put in more and more time at that hospital. In the late forties, she was working regular shifts and putting in full time . . . usually in the nursery or at a practical nurse's wage.

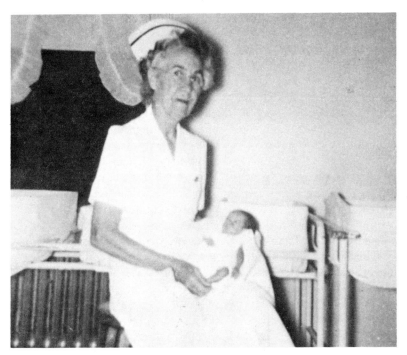

Mary E. Laing, nurse

One day Sister M. Theola, who was in charge of nurses (and perhaps the entire hospital) called the nursing mother in for a little conference. "Mary, the work you do around here and the wage I have to pay you is a little embarrassing to me. Why don't you bone up on those anatomy and psychiatric subjects and go down to Lincoln with this next class and take the State Board?" She said, "As an RN, I can pay you what you are worth to us!" Mary was flabergasted, but took the books, "boned up on them," went to Lincoln, took the "State Board" with a class of much younger people and passed it – at age 72, the oldest in the state ever to do so, at least as of that date.

Ten years later, her son, noticing she was getting frail and shakey, and thinking of the consequences should she ever drop one of those "precious bundles," had a little visit with Mother Patrice at the hospital, about it and about how they might maneuver Mary Laing out of that hospital and away from her beloved nursery without her feeling that she had been dismissed. Between the two of them it was accomplished. I guess we used some of that psychiatric training which Mother had "boned up" on some ten years before.

* * * * *

A Few Faux Pas

Carl and Herman Thalin were brothers born in Sweden and how they came to be running a blacksmith shop in Alliance in 1918 is a mystery to me. Both were very muscular, and in the hot, sooty surroundings of the forge, each seemed right at home exposing a sleeveless arm of muscles and moving with the swagger of weight lifters. Perhaps they brought that from Sweden.

Henry Fricke was German born and a carpenter, who was changing his carpenter status to that of a prominent building contractor.

Henry and Herman, the bachelor (Carl was very serious about the family he was raising) were good drinking buddies. One day they were sitting in Henry's coupe and had just finished off a pint of hooch. With not a drop left in the bottle, Herman let if fly with a powerful flip—right through the window of the car. He thought the window was open. It wasn't.

* * * * *

George Mintzer was a regular lunch customer at the Orange Tea Room, located in the Thiele Drug Store and operated by Dick Becker and Merrill Averill. Mintzer liked sugar, especially when it was well saturated with tea. He had that habit. He would order his lunch with iced tea, and then while talking, would spoon sugar into it until it failed to dissolve. This was a regular habit and Becker was getting tired of the waste. They finally had words over it, Becker must have won because George found a new place to eat lunch.

* * * * *

Whatever made me do it? My family certainly was not political minded. In fact, Dad could hardly be classed as a democrat or republican—he always said, "I vote for the best man." So why on that nice sunshiny morning in November, 1916, Election Day, did I do this thing? "This thing" was my peeking around the corner of the Emerson school building and yelling, "Hurrah for Hughes." I didn't know anything about either Hughes or Wilson, the presidential candidates, I only know that it seemed like a good idea at the time to even up the blind lopsided preference of a bunch of fourth and fifth graders for the incumbent Woodrow Wilson. I yelled and ran. It was not nearly fast enough because I was caught and soon received a bloody nose proving in playground logic that I was no political prophet.

* * * * *

One time in the bank, John Snoddy came in and made a deposit with Reuben Knight. Fred Harris, the cashier, always "worked the notes" and was busy at his desk just behind Reuben. "Ask John if he wants to put a little on that note today?" said Fred. He had raised his voice on purpose for Snoddy to hear, but there was no indication that he had. As he turned to go out the door, Reuben said, "John, Fred wants to see you." There was no response. "That old S.O.B. heard us," said Fred in a much lower voice. That time Snoddy heard the epithet, wheeled around and a real donnybrook ensued.

* * * * *

One morning I had returned from hunting and was out by the garage dressing some ducks and one white snow goose. Lige Thayer, my next door neighbor, ambled over to see what luck I'd had and upon seeing the goose, had a story. Lige was a retired rancher from north of Ellsworth. He had "come up through the ranks" one might say. That is he had been a cowboy first.

Well, Lige and another cowboy were riding horseback past a lake, when they saw a flock of white birds on the edge of ice around some open water. They had a high-powered rifle, and after careful maneuvering, got close enough to shoot and managed to hit one of the birds. They retrieved it on horseback after some little urging to enter the icy water. It was a beautiful bird, and rather proud of their marksmanship, they continued their ride, which took them through the Lawrence Bixby ranch yard.

When Lawrence saw that bird, he had to have it. It was the biggest and prettiest goose he had ever seen. He wanted it for mounting and to place on display as a trophy. The cowboys, after some little haggling, agreed to let him have it for ten dollars. Bixby was jubilant. He lost no time sending it to a taxidermist that he knew of in Lincoln.

Apparently, taxidermists are licensed and must report to the Game Commission any protected bird or animal that comes to them. The man had no choice. He reported it and rather quickly, Bixby was charged and found guilty of having a Trumpeter Swan, a protected bird, in his possession. The fine was five hundred dollars. The plea that he had not killed the bird fell upon deaf ears because initially, when admiration and envy of "the hunter" with such a fine specimen, Lawrence had left the two cowboys out of his story.

"Lige, did you give Lawrence his money back, when you saw all the grief that you had caused him?" I queried. His answer was, "Hurumph, hell no!"

* * * * *

OTHER FLASHBACKS

Age 65 was of sober significance to Marty and Edna Mae Brennan. It meant they had reached the plateau in years that marked senior citizenship. Sobering it was, but they saw fit to cover their real feelings with buffoonery. Both had applied for their Social Security benefits at the same time and knew that the checks were put in the mail for delivery on the third of each month. They pulled two rocking chairs out on the front porch, and that is the reception the mailman received – two new addressees expectantly waiting and rocking away.

* * * * *

There was a time when class day gained the same status as Halloween with Alliance high school students. Competition to have a class graduation (sic '22) flown on a banner or applied with paint to the highest and most inaccessible place was really an accomplishment. The old city water tower had many class years painted near its top, in spite of the police surveillance against the dangerous antic.

Jimmy Fowler, class of 1922, thought the symbol would be impressive atop the water tank on the three story building of Newberry's Hardware Company. When his attempt to gain the roof via the inside stairs was thwarted, he attempted to scale the outside of the building, using the indentions of the offset brick wall for his handholds. He made it almost to the top, but in contemplating how he would get over the edge above him, he made the mistake of looking down and froze. He could go neither up or down. A large crowd gathered to watch the rescue. In those days, the fire department had no equipment to work that high. After a breathtaking thirty minutes, with tension and apprehension mounting, the harness makers on the third floor managed to literally "snake" the lad through a window and the Alliance business district went back to its normal day.

* * * * *

Joe Pozza had a hardware store on West Third Street in Alliance during the 1940s. He had one item, the Superfex Oil Burner, which he stressed in all his advertising. Before the city had its own KCOW radio station in 1949, Wednesday was "Alliance Day" on one of the

Scottsbluff stations. Local advertisers were solicited to buy time and Joe was a regular, with one stipulation. He insisted on announcing his own message. Joe went to great length to extoll the virtues of that heating plant. His speech was slightly broken, between Italian and English, so his words and ideas were often tolerated with great amusement by the listener. One of his patented messages went something like this: "Superfex, that safe and economical type of heating – hot air goes up, cold air goes down. That's one law that even Mr. Roosevelt could not repeal!"

* * * * *

Cy Laing and his favorite sport on Bronco Lake.

My Dad always retained his membership in Alliance Country Club. Perhaps he would have anyhow, but the main reason was that it provided him with a safe place to tie up his scow which he used for hunting. One morning when out on the lake, he gave up hunting in disgust because the day had dawned bright and clear and without any wind. About the only birds on the lake was a tremendous migration of mud hens, or coots, which had come onto the lake at night. The lake's surface was smooth and glassy as Dad rowed the old boat quietly and without a splash from the oars into the concentration of curious birds. Carefully, he laid down the oars and picked up his automatic. The mud hens gave him a bit more room with that, but were reluctant to fly and just sort of paddled out of the boat's path.

When a few of them did take off, it was a signal to Dad that that picture was not going to last forever, so he blasted into the escaping birds now frantically running across the water to get take-off momentum, mowing them down as if he had a maching gun in his hands. I forget how many he picked up.

As he rowed up to the pier, an old darky, who the clubhouse committee had employed to cater meals and live temporarily in the clubhouse, came ambling down to meet him. "What luck Mr. Laing?" he queried. A mischievous thought crossed Cy's mind. "Say Josh, do you all want some black duck?" "Deed I do, Mr. Laing, 'deed I do," and as fifteen or twenty mud hens were laid out on the pier, Josh took possession of them with profuse thanks.

Meanwhile, there was a Banker's convention in Alliance, and rather than being content with the luncheon menu it offered, Brad Minor, Vice-president of the First National Bank and a man of impeccable taste, decided to take a small party of visiting bankers to the club for lunch. They had a few drinks and Brad addressed the old darky with, "Anything special for lunch, Josh?" The answer was, "Yas'r Mister Minor – Black Duck." The special was agreeable to all and when served, was relished as a delicacy. Had anyone of those men realized they were eating mudhen, it is doubtful if his meal would have been finished.

* * * * *

Uncle Beany is mentioned elsewhere in these pages, as has been the Krause home lake. Once while hunting there with him late in the fall, the lake was partially frozen and most of the ducks had migrated on to the south. I did manage to knock down a nice big canvasback drake. He fell out on the edge of the ice, just a few feet from open water. Hunting was slow, and from my vantage point, behind a muskrat house, the beautiful markings and plumage, glistening in the sunlight were too much for me. I had to have that duck. I undressed completely, got back into my boots, which without socks were roomy and could be shed quickly, if necessary, and gingerly worked my way out to that bird on that not-too-thick ice. As I reached to pick it up, I actually could feel the rubbery ice sinking with my weight, but by sliding instead of stepping, and giving my four or five pound prize a mighty heave onto more solid ice, I managed to get back to the rat house and my clothes without breaking

111

through the ice and no worse off for my foolishness than a bunch of goose pimples on a body of pink skin.

Uncle Beany? He had witnessed me, naked as a jay bird, from a distance and was not too happy about my bravado.

* * * * *

Qualifications for a Public Employee? I worked for the public for many years, but I tried not to be typed by Frank Broome's definition. Frank had been in the government land office for many years and later, was a long-time police judge so he should know the qualifications. His version was relatively simple—"to just sit on one's butt and holler for more help!"

* * * * *

One of my first jobs, I had just turned twelve, was working for Bert Duncan in his grocery store. One morning I had been de-tailed to help Butch (I don't think I ever did know his full name) grind hamburger. Butch had the meat ready for the electric grinder and the idea was to feed the fat and suet evenly with the lean meat for obvious reasons. He had a small pile of the finished product and just as he was turning away from the grinder, to give me my turn in the operation, he gave a particularly stubborn piece of meat a poke and mangled his hand terribly. In fact, the grinder complete-ly severed his thumb.

There was great excitement around the butcher shop and a lot of blood. Bert rushed the poor man to Dr. Bellwood's office above Holsten's Drug Store for that was close. The hand was dressed, but with the shock of the whole matter, Butch wasn't able to and didn't come back to work. When the excitement had died down in the store, Bert noticed the hamburger operation had not been com-pleted. "Can you finish that Bob?" he asked. "Yes, I think so," I replied and proceeded to justify the confidence just put in me. When finished, the hamburger was mounded up in a neat pile on a flat pan and put in the display case.

I stood back and admired my work; it was as good as Butch might have done. Butch? My gosh, where was that thumb? I said nothing, but in cleaning up that back room I looked and looked for that missing appendage, but to no avail. By that time, I was too scared of the consequences that might be entailed with spoiling a whole batch of hamburger. So I said nothing. Perhaps, if anyone noticed any strange taste, they might reason that a piece of veal had been added in its preparation.

* * * * *

Prohibition Era

There have been bootleggers in the United States long before the Volstead Act and the adoption of the Eighteenth Amendment to the Constitution. This happened to be a very unpopular law with many people feeling that it was an encroachment on their personal liberty. Therefore, they (and "they" were often the very pillars of the community) were, in many cases, ready to pay the price of prohibited items, and to risk reputations to a point where enforcement became a farce. Under those conditions, there are always those persons willing to take a chance to "turn an easy buck" especially in times of depression or artificial prosperity like during the "golden years of the twenties."

Before this period, bootlegging was more or less confined to the business of escaping the government tax imposed on distilleries. The moonshiner was, while quite an object of the federal agents (usually spread too thin to be effective) might be good friends and neighbors with local officials. Prohibition made an entirely new game of things and there was shortly after its creation in 1919, probably as many or more "stills" in the Nebraska sandhills as in the entire fabled Cumberland and Appalachian mountain areas.

Such were the circumstances in connection with the confiscation of one of the county's first stills. Tom Gray was a well-known bootlegger. Local officers tried for months to locate the supply of Tom's illicit booze. One day, apparently on a tip from someone who didn't like Tom, or was jealous of him or perhaps on the promise of a reward, officers located Tom's still and brought it to town as evidence.

Sheriff Jim Miller was quite proud of his catch and reasoned that if people could just see where what they were drinking came from, no one in Alliance would ever again buy a bottle of "rot gut." Arrangements were made to display the still and its contents, just as the officers found them, in the large window in the front of Lowery and Henry garage, now Dobson Motors. This was a prominent location. Sooner or later, everyone walked by this window and would see the display. It was thought also that it would make an impression on school children, especially the high school youth, who were just about to join their elders in scoff-lawing, drinking.

The idea was great. Sheriff Miller's motive, to impress adult and teenager alike, was of the best intention, but it is my opinion that both adult and teenager were unimpressed even with the unsavory odor and appearance of the soured mashed in the large vat, "seasoned" with a half dozen dead rats that had not been able to scale the metal sides of the vat and escape. Most believed what they wanted to believe – that the distillation process between the rotten mess and the finished product purified the end product, making it safe enough to drink.

* * * * *

By the 1930's, the art of distilling had been considerably improved. Burr Underwood was reputed "to have about as good booze" as could be purchased. Ross Sampson liked to tell of the time he and three other men were going goose hunting west of Alliance in the Good Streak country. An early start was in order for they had a long way to go and it was imperative to be settled in a pit by sunrise.

Their route took them past Burr's place and all four thought they should have a "jug" to help them through a long day of waiting, so they stopped and aroused Burr. He was not too happy at being aroused between three and four o'clock in the morning, but with a terse order of, "Okay, you guys stay here," he disappeared in the darkness and in time came back with a jug.

Much later that day, in fact it was long after dark on a moonless night, the hunters were returning. Someone observed that they were out of booze and should stop again at Burr's. Another said, "Well, we know where he keeps it – in that cornfield right by the house. Let's just find it ourselves and not bother old Burr." It was pitch dark but after kicking and prodding blindly around the cornstalks looking for the cache, someone exclaimed, "I found it. Let's get the hell out of here!" Back at the car there was great merriment over the success of their prank. In the inky darkness they almost had to feel instead of see. After the jug was passed around, the pranksters piled into the car, quite talkative.

One in the back seat chided his companion with, "get over, there was plenty of room back here before we got out." Any probably there was, for now there were five. Old Burr had them figured out and after a day of waiting for them, and probably out of lonesomeness, he joined them. He needed some company and one can only guess who found the booze.

* * * * *

Jimmy Graham and Ralph Silver were a couple of the town's "young blades." They were never in real bad trouble, but did have a record of pranks and mischief – usually with a liquor connection.

114

George Barnum on police motorcycle, circa 1935

One night they were under suspicion for having liquor in their possession and were being chased by Officers Barnum and Doty, who were
on the police motorcycle and sidecar.

The two pursued swung their car into the curb and entered the
Maryland Cafe until "things cooled down a little." For some reason,
Jimmy returned to the car just as the motorcycle turned in alongside
their car. The two officers consulted briefly and then entered the
cafe to accost the two "scoff-laws." Jimmy moved fast and transferred two bottles of booze from the car to the motorcycle and then
nonchalantly followed the police, who were questioning Silver about
Jimmy's absence.

There ensued quite a discussion much to the entertainment of
the other restaurant patrons. There were questions, denials, accusa-
tions and much asserted innocence. Then the four left the place to
inspect the car of the accused. Quite a few bystanders gathered
around too. When no liquor was found in the car, Graham and Silver,
of course could not be held, so in a great display of offended dignity,
they departed with an assumed air of violated rights, "the hell with
this, let's get going!"

When the officers started to leave the scene, there wasn't room
for two bottles and Doty's big feet in the bottom of the sidecar,
but after a short conference during which they didn't see one dependable witness in the prejudiced crowd of spectators, they gave up
any further idea of arrest.

* * * * *

One time Mayor Kenneth (Dobby) Lee was telling me about his
plans to remodel the farm house he had purchased at the north
end of the then county road, now an extension of Sweetwater Avenue.

115

I thought a moment and then observed, "I know that place. It used to belong to Clyde Rust. In fact, I have patronized Clyde, who liked to supplement a rather poorly operated farm's income with a little bootlegging." I went on describing how Clyde was raided many times, but was never caught with any whiskey on the place. It was in the sheriff's jurisdiction, being outside of the city limits. Then I told him of my experiences. "I would go out to make a purchase (usually for a Saturday night boost) and the house would be dark. I'd knock and pretty soon Clyde would push open the door and eye me questioningly, because he still associated my Dad with law enforcement.

'Who's with you?' he would ask, indicating the waiting car. Then I would make my purchase, after he had stepped back into the house alone. He always had booze there, but it could not be located by the officers in a raid."

The several weeks later, Dobby called me at the office saying, "If you can get away for a bit, I have something out here of interest to you." I said, "Sure, I'll be right out. Want to see your place anyhow." Well, what Dobby had to show me explained a lot. He had progressed in his remodeling to some work on the stairs. Up several steps from the living room, neatly concealed by the carpet runner was a riser with a trap door neatly opening into a compartment that could hold quite a supply of "bottled goods" – a thirty year old secret, well kept.

* * * * *

In this story, like in the FBI serial of early day television, "only the names have been changed to protect the innocent." We will call our principal, Jake.

Jake was a railroad engineer, now retired. Back in the thirties, he supplemented his wages with some "ill-gotten gains." I really don't think that he was so shackled financially so much as he just enjoyed living dangerously. However, railroad layoffs were common in those days, so perhaps the earnings from bootlegging were a welcome supplement. Jake lived just beyond the city limits and his specialty was home brewed beer.

Before I was married, it was a "big deal" to go up to Jake's and guzzle a bottle of home brew, usually from a pan or kettle rather than from a glass. We'd sit there on improvised seats and drink our "suds" in his dug basement which had no flooring or walls, barely lighted by a ten watt bulb on the end of an extension cord. Pretty soon someone would say, "Jake, why don't you give us some more light?" Jake's answer would be, "Buy another round and I'll screw in a bigger bulb."

* * * * *

Inter-city golf matches used to be popular at the Country Club. On one occasion, Alliance was entertaining Sidney. Blaine Beckwith and the writer were the entertainment committee. As expected of us, we had a horse tank full of ice cooling some five dozen quarts of home brewed beer and some jugs of whiskey.

The Country Club had only nine holes for a golf course, so we didn't commence our play until everyone else was paired up and playing. The timing was just right—the starting foursome was on number nine green as we were about to tee off on number one tee. As they came across our fairway before we hit, to quench their thirsts at the clubhouse, we told them to help themselvs to the refreshments and where they were, in the driveway under the building. Before we had proceeded very far down our fairway, one of the men came running out and asked if that beer was all right? Of course Blaine and I thought it was all right, but we followed back to check things out. One fellow had just taken a big swallow, but was trying to extricate something stringy from his teeth. A close examination of "the thing" proved it to be a piece of sauerkraut— everyone had his own recipe for settling yeast. That sauerkraut was Mary Verjaski's, the old Italian lady's method. She supplied us with the beer.

* * * * *

For someone to mention Ed Slaughter in Alliance might bring out some questioning looks, but had the mention been to Sparkplug or Sparky Slaughter, recognition would have been instant. And therein lies another illustration of the legal lassitude in the prosecutions of liquor violations during the days of prohibition. It caused a lot of grumbling among city, county and state officers, who felt that they "stuck their necks out" to make arrests that might never be prosecuted to a conclusion.

Sparky Slaughter was definitely "King" of the black underworld in Alliance in the twenties and thirties. The Slaughter family was an old one in the city. Abstracts of title to a number of properties south of Third Street and particularly in West Lawn (that area west of the railroad tracks and south of Third Street) will reflect Slaughter ownership in many cases.

For years, Sparky had ownership interest in 101 Sweetwater, which was an "alleged" house of ill repute. It served as a cafe, house of prostitution, gambling and rooming house and was definitely a "nigger dive" where anything goes and usually did. It was shunned by decent blacks and white people alike.

Over "101" Sparky reigned, but occasionally he would slip and be brought into court. This was usually for selling or possessing bootleg liquor. Invariably Sparky would be just about on the ropes with the court, when his attorney would present LeRoy Abbott, President of The Guardian State Bank, to the court to vouch for Ed Slaughter's good character. There was no judge, jury or prosecutor that was going to argue that point with LeRoy Abbott, so Sparky would be dismissed and live to sin another day.

* * * * *

Could Have Beens

Prairie Airlines, a brainchild of Christopher Abbott, operated in western Nebraska to the state's eastern cities like Omaha, Lincoln and Grand Island. The long range concept was that this feeder line would expand and become a trunk line, the first direct air service between Seattle and Miami. In 1948, the first step was almost accomplished. The award of a mail contract by the government was a certainty for Prairie, except it was delayed on account of the election year. Politics.

A few of the stockholders in Prairie Airlines

Chris, Prairie's president, had worked hard on the mail thing, but found that patronage played a big part in high postal decisions. His stature nationally practically assured the Prairie designation and approval as a mail carrier. It certainly would have been a financial windfall for the struggling young company, but for one thing. Chris became so enraptured with and convinced that Thomas E. Dewey would defeat Harry S. Truman, and become the 33rd elected President of the United States, that he backed rash statements with large wagers in high places. When Truman polled 303 electoral votes to Dewey's 189, it was an upset victory, which caused Chris to "throw in the towel" as far as the airline's chances of getting any of the spoils. Dissolution of the corporation was commenced at once.

* * * * *

Works Progress Administration (WPA) and Public Works Administration (PWA) were emergency measures of Franklin D. Roosevelt's administration, designed to create jobs for the 12,000,000 unemployed in 1933.

Alliance benefited from both. The City Hall and Auditorium, completed in 1936, was a PWA project. There were dozens of WPA projects of less dollar involvement, but of quicker relief to the local unemployed. These included park improvement, street improvement and other activities, which under local direction within certain federal guidelines, reimbursed the city.

By 1940 both programs were phased out. In appreciation of favors and cooperation of the local director and engineers, a farewell dinner was held at the Alliance Country Club. As men gathered in groups on the screened porch of the clubhouse, someone observed that it was too bad that Bronco Lake could not have been developed to give the community a dependable, fresh water reservoir. Clarence H. Hoper, then city manager, had made a study of this and determined that it would take the output of four, one thousand gallon, irrigation wells to maintain the lake's level on account of evaporation and perculation. Then the cost of acquiring right-of-way and construction of the canal to provide an outlet to the lake into the Snake Creek valley, a couple of miles to the south, would be too prohibitive and the matter had been dropped.

When the State Director heard of that, he regretted that the matter had not been brought to their attention. Apparently, the cost or feasibility of a project was no deterrent to these men. It was often said by critics, that if FDR wanted a mountain moved, he simply had it relocated.

* * * * *

B. B. Wright purchased the Alliance Country Club property from its stockholders and operated it as a Supper Club for several years. He often observed the wasted food left on the tables by his patrons just to be thrown away. Bill considered starting a hog farm just west of the clubhouse. He felt the waste would make a profitable supplement in hog feeding – just another thing that didn't get done.

* * * * *

A tragedy was averted one time in the Alliance Creamery, due to the watchful eye and quick reaction of Earl Meyer, who as a young college student, was employed by the creamery during school holidays. A young child, little more than a toddler, wandered too close and fell into the freight elevator well on the first floor. The elevator had been loaded upstairs, and just as it began its descent, Meyers grasped the situation and with no hesitation, dived into the well, picked up the errant lad and scrambled out. Both could have been crushed to death, which would have meant the loss of two brilliant people-to-be.

The rescuer lived to practice law and become the panhandle's long time District Judge, the Hon. Earl L. Meyer; the rescued lad, Verne M. Laing, grew up and became a prominent attorney in Wichita, Kansas.

* * * * *

With the Horn

The Kosmet Klub was an unofficial University organization, very unofficial in fact, tolerated on the campus chiefly because it was committed to producing a fun show annually. The 1927 Review was an outstanding production. Musically, original songs and tunes by such talent as Harold Turner, Harriet Kruse Kemmerer, Joyce Ayres and usually sung by Jack Wheelock, revealed exceptional talent. The acting, carefully cued with touching love songs, was acceptable. The chorus line, if one can imagine Blue Howell, Glen Presnell and about ten other thick-legged football players high-kicking like starlets, was a bit short of ever making Broadway, but it was fun.

I was asked to play trombone in the "pit" orchestra. Rehearsals were riotous and performances were played during Christmas vacation in some eight towns and cities in eastern Nebraska, winding down the tour on Christmas Eve in the auditorium of Tech High School in Omaha. Of course, we first had a practice sesssion on the penitentiary inmates, which brings us to my experience at the pen.

Arriving early, the orchestra was held up until the inmates were all seated. We were then motioned to take our places, with instruments of course, below and in front of the stage. I was in the midst of the group, most of whom had not been in the pen before. Suddenly, from the seated prisoners on the right of the aisle, came a loud voice, "Hey dere Laing. How's yo' Dad?" I turned to see a really black, black man motioning me expectantly. I didn't know him but paused to pass the time of day for courtesy sake. I was immediately challenged by a guard, who suggested that I take my instrument and case to the front and then return to visit, if I wished. I did. This fellow, I can't even recall his name, was a lifer, sent up for an axe murder in the Alliance stockyards. Dad was Deputy Sheriff at the time and discovered the man cringing behind one of the large swinging gates between the planked runway and the animal pens. Dad arrested him and escorted him to jail. Neither man was armed.

While "reporting" to the murderer, I was then hailed by another inmate. This was Urban Zediker from Alliance, who was doing time for his part in the robbery of the Fashion Shop, a local ladies ready-to-wear store. Urban was a well known underworld character who just never had hit the big time. He was a handwriting expert and I remember Christmas cards, with large fancy scrolls and greetings, that Dad received from him for years. Dad would recognize whom the card was from without ever slitting the envelope.

122

Then a third man hailed me. This was six foot five Ed Lewis. He had worked as a dishwasher in one of Dad's cafes, but was serving time for his part in that same Fashion Shop robbery. It was said that because of his height and strength, he had hoisted an accomplice up and through a transom to gain access from inside the store.

Well, so much for my "friends." When I returned to the orchestra pit, I was aware of the looks cast at me and of those between the fellows. "What kind of a guy have we got here in our midst?" I admit it was a little strange but the show went on.

After the Omaha show, I caught Burlington train No. 41 and was home Christmas morning.

* * * * *

University of Nebraska also had good tough football teams back in the 1920's and in the old Big Six conference. In 1926 the squad came up to Thanksgiving Day with a 6-1-0 record and a game with the University of Washington. In 1925, the two teams had battled to a 6-6 tie in Lincoln. Spirits were high and a special train was promoted for the return engagement to be played in Seattle. Nebraska's 90 piece ROTC marching band was included in the party.

There was a fraternity party the night of departure and although we were not together at the party, a dental student by name of Claude Elwell and I "cut it a little too fine," getting to the train at 11:30 p.m. We made it just as the iron gates between the old passenger depot and the trains clanged shut and the red tail light on the train's last car was disappearing into the darkness of the railroad yards. We were two very disconsolate band members to have been left behind.

I went home and slipped into the back door of the Fraternity house. I didn't care to have to make the explanation that I knew would be demanded by the brothers. I made it, prepared for bed and crawled into my top bunk for a fitfull night's sleep. I was awakened by someone yelling up the stairs to "Get Laing on the phone!"

"He isn't here. He went to Seattle," was answered.

"Yes he is. He missed the train and this is the Burlington ticket office." Thank goodness the downstairs voice belonged to a persistent owner. Eventually, a couple of the brothers checked me out, found that Laing was there, that he was not on his way to Seattle because he had missed the train. The phone caller was not on hold all that time but the fellows relayed me the message, that there were two tickets for Laing and Elwell waiting at the ticket office and not to miss tonight's No. 41. We didn't.

Elwell and I went to the depot together, picked up our tickets, which were for first class passage, including pullman, all the way. The kindly ticket agent thought it was a hell of a joke and even let us read the message, which had been wired from Belmont, Nebraska, and was signed by John K. Selleck.

Alliance is 365 railroad miles from Lincoln and the first stop of any consequence for the special train at about 4:00 a.m. Due to the enthusiasm of Earl D. Mallery, a Nebraska alumnus and prominent citizen, there had been quite some turnout expecting to see a couple of Alliance boys in the Nebraska contingent. Frank Dailey was on the squad and I was in the band. Of course the Laing family was there in force. Their dejection and disappointment was pitiful.

Mallery had solicited quite a number of wild ducks from local hunters to present to the official party and Cy Laing had been a heavy contributor. Apparently, the turnout of Alliance fans, the ducks and the obvious disappointment of the Laing family was cause for a consultation resulting in Mr. Selleck's wire from Belmont, some 60 miles northwest of Alliance. While the Laing family met early morning trains on successive days, the second morning must have been anticlimactic to them but the occasion was great and the "boo boo" was soon put in its proper perspective and could be laughed at. Elwell and I continued our trip, joining the party in Seattle one day late, but in time for most of the fun, pomp and hospitality that usually goes with a holiday game.

Oh yes, the game. It was another bruiser, but this time it was played in the rain on a muddy sod field. Nebraska lost 6-10, which was disappointing of course, but the program included a scenic side trip to Portland and the Columbia River drive. Waterfront exposure and quantities of seafood were most impressive to a bunch of youngsters. This was in 1926 and most of them had never been out of the state of Nebraska before. The route home included a stopover in Denver and a reception by Colorado Alumni.

We had hardly settled down to campus routine when I was being kidded by some of the brothers that I was now in pictures and really did get to Seattle. I found out what they were talking about and found someone to go to a matinee at the Lincoln theater. We made it in time to catch the Pathe News and sure enough – there was old Laing, trombone and all, in the front line leading the parade in the Nebraska band.

* * * * *

Marijuana is certainly a serious health problem in the country today, but it was not an unknown substance in the nineteen twenties and thirties. Its use was often associated with musicians, particularly members of traveling bands. Long jumps between bookings, lack of sleep and fatigue contributed to the need for a "lift." After a few such experiences, with apparent success, whether actual or imagined, a user could and many times did fall into the habit of using "the weed."

Somehow, I escaped the use of marijuana even though some of my fellow musicians used it. I was lucky and have always credited my mother's influence. She was a nurse and I had great respect for her knowledge and know-how about such things. Her frankness and honesty had a deep-seated effect on me. She counseled me one time that, "I know you will be tempted playing in orchestras to take a drink and you'll take it on occasion because that's apparently in our (the Roberts) blood, but don't, please don't ever take your first taste of dope in any form," and on and on until I guess the picture of an old Chinaman attending "the needs" of men lying in bunks in a smoked-filled opium den was impressed effectively on me. Sometimes the escaping vapor from exhaled marijuana smoke made me apprehensive. Certainly all musicians do not use the stuff, and for those that do, it is too bad they didn't have a similar influence.

* * * * *

Frank (Razzy) Rathburn was one of those piano players, who upon hearing a tune could sit down and play it, almost instantly supplying the proper chords and giving the melody that sock, beat and rhythm that so many legitimate players lack and never do learn. A country club dance was a frequent job for our little local band, and with Razzy at the piano, many dancers would stop and invite us, one and all for a drink, usually at intermission. On one ocassion, a new supply of booze must have been imported into the community because the invitations came fast and furious. Cogswell, Threlkeld and I did not partake of these opportunities because we were number one, too young, and number two, our folks were usually there because dancing was a popular form of recreation for them.

On this occasion Razzy was a little late getting back from "downstairs" after intermission. We were getting nervous because we needed his piano, rhythm and know-how. Finally, he appeared and needless to say, he was drunk. Then we noticed something else. He was bleeding freely from one hand, which he had cut on a broken glass. Sympathy and offers of first aid went unheeded – he was ready to play and did. Before the first piece was finished, that piano had a red and black keyboard. Razzy said he couldn't play with a bandaged hand and he went on to finish the night with that bloody mess.

* * * * *

One of our orchestra's favorite places to play was in the County Fair pavilion at Mitchell, Nebraska. It was managed by the American Legion and was patronized by dancers from all over the panhandle. The management was aggressive and booked many "name" bands. Herbie Kaye and his band, complete with Dorothy Lamour singing the love ballads, had played there the previous Saturday night and the Legion could not book a local band to follow — so great was the Kaye performance.

Harold Smith, our manager and leader, received a call to play that Saturday night. The Scottsbluff County Legion was desperate. Smith was young and brash and as we all wished we could break into playing at that dance hall, a substitute was arranged for the date we already had and after beefing up our band with a second entertainer, adding another saxophone and a bass, away we went to brave the favor or disfavor of a critical dance crowd. Apparently, the Smith Brothers orchestra made a good impression because a grateful Legion dance committee favored us with a number of bookings after that.

VII

MUD, SNOW AND GEESE was accepted by
and published in the November 1982 issue of
NEBRASKAland, the outdoor magazine
published by the Nebraska Game and Parks
Commission. It was the writer's first published
story.

Mud, Snow and Geese

The hunting season in the Nebraska Panhandle had been a frustrating one. The lakes, mostly saucers of water with a high content of alkali and other salts, without outlets or inlets, normally received enough runoff to hold their levels through the hot summers until the winter snowfall. This year was an exception. There was drought, which of course might vary from year to year; but a more sinister forewarning to the duck hunter was the lowering of water table much faster than the underground recharge. This was caused by pump irrigation which had increased several hundred percent in agricultural practice which twenty years before had been only experimental.

Historically, the Nebraska sandhills have always produced thousands of ducks and other migrators annually. They still offer good nesting habitat in the spring of the year. But by the time the broods are able to fly, the above conditions, added to the natural perculation and because of evaporation due to the hot, dry Nebraska winds of July and August, the hundreds and hundreds of waterfilled lakes and ponds have then become mud flats and are abandoned by the larger web-footed birds, leaving only the snipe, rail, bittern and plover to eke out an existance from the parched, cracked lake bottom of what had been a safe, comfortable and inviting body of water for the spring migration. The duck broods mentioned then "flock up" and most move to the larger spring-fed lakes, like those found in the Garden County reserve, or to the North Platte or Niobrara Rivers.

Before these conditions came about, the sandhills offered a flyway to the northern migrators that lasted from early October through December. In the early days this flyway was highly commercialized by the market hunter. The chain of dams along the upper Missouri River contribute somewhat to ths change in the flyway pattern, but logically should make for an orderly release of migrating flocks through the lake country as of yore, if it could offer more than these dried up, alkali lake beds, instead of hurrying them down the Missouri River gauntlet of hunters, to their winter homes.

Whoever said a mournful dirge was the way to attract readers and to invite them to begin a story about two hunting-starved men with a successful hunt to climax a so-so season? No one I'm sure, but that was the situation and the reason for my good friend Oley

Saylor and I deciding upon a goose hunt along the North Platte River in an attempt to salvage something from a disappointing season.

Barry Balka, a businessman-farmer from Lisco, Nebraska, was in the Alliance Elks Club one day late in the autumn and we got to talking about hunting. Barry has a meadow and leases a couple of other pieces of land, on which he builds blinds or pits and rents them out by the day during the goose season. These are along the river, which is a reserve, and the blinds must be at least 20 rods from its nearest channel. Anyhow, arrangements were made for a blind late in November – somehow Oley and I had conflicts until then, but anyhow, we had a place arranged to go to.

Normally I took my car because I have the decoys and they were all loaded. Oley is one of my favorite breakfast chefs. He cooks that thick-sliced bacon just right and turns out a couple of eggs apiece just to my liking with toast, hot coffee and, oh yes ketchup for me – the bottle has probably been in his "frig" since my last breakfast visit. Well, this morning we passed up this breakfast offering to "get down the road aways." We would grab something at the little cafe in Broadwater. The word was out. The geese were in. No less authority than the *Omaha World-Herald* sport page said so. We were really psyched up and after that fifty mile drive, hungry. That cafe was something else. It wasn't just crowded; it was jammed with hunters. There was a Minneapolis paper's sports editor, writers from several sporting magazines and representatives of several urban newspapers. All had "the word." The geese were in and they all wanted a piece of the action, the kill, the stuff about which a successful hunting trip is written. For some it was all in a days work but I'm sure that for some others it bid fair to be a high pointed reward to a hard-earned vacation.

We finally were served and stowed away a hearty breakfast – ham and eggs with "hash browns," steaming hot coffee and of course my ketchup. We each had a quart thermos to fill with coffee to supplement the brown-bag lunch that would help pass the expected day of waiting. We always took care of man's nutritional requirements one way or another. Then, as if a signal for all, someone announced the time and that little cafe was vacated by the entire crowd of expectant hunters. We were the last to leave and were of course apprehensive that there wouldn't be a goose left for us.

For several minutes Broadwater, population 141, had traffic problems as cars were started and drivers vied for position on Hiway 26, like drivers in a race each coveting the pole position. Some had only a short trip before turning off to the river and to their blinds. Our trip was a little longer but only, through Lisco, 12 miles, and about four miles further to "a certain gate at a fence intersection just across the road from a farmhouse." We wondered if Barry had scheduled us for a two-man pit or if we would be sharing a larger blind with others just as goose hungry as we.

It was pitch dark so we pull off the road and waited. It was beginning to spit some small hard snow pellets but we could see car lights, followed by another pair, bobbing across the meadow, and knew that would be Barry stationing his paying guests. Finally the pairs of headlights separated. One bobbed and swerved its way back away from the river (that would be one of the hunters parking the car) and then its lights were extinguished. The other pair of lights bobbed but came steadily towards us (that had to be Barry) and it was. When he got out of the pickup and recognized us for the first time, there was frustration in his manner and an expression of combined dismay and embarrassment on his face, even in the half-light of the cars. "Bob, why didn't you confirm this with me? I just filled my last blind and I can't squeeze you in anywhere," he apologized. Our dissappointment showed too. I, of course, thought a couple of weeks was assurance enough to hold our arrangement but this was like confirming one's airline tickets and flight. What a feeling of despair – an eighty mile trip and no place to set down for the day almost surely meant the eighty mile return trip would be a very silent one.

But Barry was thinking. He fully appreciated our situation. "Tell you what," he said, "I've got a twenty acre barley stubble just across the hiway and railroad tracks that I didn't bother to put a blind on, but this snow is picking up so that one place may be as good as another today. If you want to dig a shallow pit, I've got two shovels. You can throw the dirt in the pickup. I'll wait for you and just dump it back in the hole tomorrow. I may need the weight for ballast before this day is done and, there will be no charge." We quickly agreed to the arrangement and followed the pickup into an unusually short stubble field. Barry located the site; Oley and I went to work. The snow had picked up in intensity; the flakes were big and heavy. They came almost straight down and we had the feeling that a pretty good snowfall was setting in.

My partner was at home with a shovel, which was comforting. It showed his eagerness for action was equal to mine; and the activity eased my feeling of guilt. Mid flying scoops full, Barry kept up encouraging conversation. There were some reference to Digger O'Dell of radio fame (I believe that was the Fibber McGee program) and with other good natured small talk, we finally had a pit and Barry had a load of dirt which was fast becoming mud. We quit digging, unloaded the 24 stuffed canvas decoys and our lunch and hunting paraphernalia in the same pile. Oley sorted it out while I followed

Barry to a nearside of the field, where the car would be nearly out of sight, not from above perhaps if the weather cleared, but at the eye level, yes. And then, it was now shooting time and some perfection had to be sacrificed for rushed expediency. I legged it back to the blind as Barry parted with "Good luck—see 'ya."

Oley hadn't touched the decoys (he knew I liked to place them even though we usually had the same conception on the appearance of the spread). His arrangement of the stuff in the pit looked satisfactory to me, and that was no small bit of comfort because it was really snowing now and I could see he had covered the paper bags, shells and small items with a tarp—not too large a tarp, and things were already getting muddy.

I was just turning to place a decoy when there came to our ears, that spine-tingling "a-lunk k-lunk" of geese, What to do? There was no time to set out decoys now. This flock, although we couldn't see them, had to be partically on top of us, so dive into the pit it was, and from here on, I shall refer to it as our mud hole. There was no time to adjust for comfort. We assured each other it was past time to shoot. Here they were upon us! What a picture first, the outstretched necks, open mouths of each bird emitting the goose-jargon that has excited hunters down through the ages, and that multiplied by probably twenty in the flock; next, they were right over us, the canvas grey of the under-bellies of the big birds startling and ghost-like in the backdrop of falling snow. As of one mind, we fired in what seemed only an instant that they were visible and

Ghosts

the opportunity offered. We were rewarded by two distinct thuds as two heavy bodies fell from the flock, which was now gone almost as spookily and eerily as it had appeared. No doubt it was a flock lost in the storm, for conditions were just not right for geese to attempt feeding in such a blinding storm.

The two geese lay still. Excitement and shock of the moment hit us both. Then we laughed crazily and pounded each other on the back as if there had just been a winning field goal, or basket or whatever scored. We crouched there in disbelief and decided the occasion called for a shot of hot coffee. Getting a thermos bottle open and pouring a cupful brought home to us what the day was going to be like, if we stayed. We had two geese, the decoys hadn't even been put out and it was impossible to keep the mud out of anything, especially the grooved, spiral necks of the screw cap of the thermos, and the day-old lunch – it was a soaked disaster. Well enough of such realization. Do we stay for more or pull stakes? Well, at least the price was right; the vote was affirmative and unanimous to stay.

We put the decoys out "to stay just a little while longer." We bunched them facing what wind there was and divorced two off from the side of the flock. Some say that is always a good setup as it looks more natural to incoming birds. I don't know that to be a fact but I have done it that way for years. Anyhow, with the decoys out, we returned to the mud hole and passed the time with small talk, coffee, cleaning our glasses and poking fun at our general muddied appearance. Oh yes, and occasionally fondling the thick down breasts of our two birds.

It must have snowed hard for another hour or more and then gradually subsided. We could now see the fencing on two sides of the field and an occasional car edging along the hiway. We occasionally joked about "the Spirit of Gering," a derisive through affectionate tag, the natives hung on the local combined passenger and freight train that plied the Union Pacific branch line between North Platte and Gering daily (some days) and speculated as to whether it would even run this day. Suddenly we realized the sun had broken through the overcast and was now blinding bright. Sure, one might know – both of our colored glasses had been left in the car. Oley lost the flip and went after them because they were really needed in the glare of the white wonderworld that surrounded us. I knocked snow off decoys and rearranged them in some cases. Both back to our mud hole, we realized it was a strange and silent world – visibility was now several miles but not a hunter was to be seen, and not a single shot except ours had been fired all morning. All was a penetrating silence, almost an apprehensive one.

Suddenly, there was life on the river! I've mentioned that we were hunting just off the reserve and the great concentration of Canadas down east of us had decided to move. Although we knew the hunters were there, there was no movement or shots in the, perhaps, three miles of river front that we could see from our commanding location. We knew they were there, crouched down and ready in frozen immobility, just as we were, as that mass of noisy birds jockeyed up the river's channels, following the lead birds and definitely going out to feed in the fields north and west of this stretch of reserve. I know if there could have been a nose count, there were 150 to 200 hunters in the breadth of the panorama we commanded, but not one shot was fired.

What causes the leaders, after attaining the desired altitude, to pick a point from which to leave the river, no one knows, but everyone out that day watched that huge flock of several thousand birds pick such a point and gangle noisily off to the northwest in search of a craw full of corn.

We knew the area, and in about fifteen minutes, as expected, we heard a bombardment coming from the table country where our wily feathered friends had chosen to dine. From the intensity of the bombardment, it was a fair guess that fewer birds would return to the river than went out. And return they did, honking and literally scrambling back, high and out of range, to the safety of the river, and then tumbling down in spectacular abandon from the safety of the altitude that took them away from the river a half hour before to the safety of the willow covered islands and sandbars of the river reserve. Oh yes, now there were a few futile and frustrating shots taken in desperation as the geese returned, but not a bird tumbled to a gun. Shortly the quiet returned and with it again wonderment as to whether we should leave and call it a day. It appeared the show was over for that day. We sat there in our hole, silent unto our own thoughts, enjoying the beauty of nature and reliving the scene provided by those majestic wild birds. Neither wanted to be the one to suggest quitting the hunt but we were not comfortable. In fact, we were chilled from the wet as our clothes absorbed the damp of melting snow, and any movement on our part commenced a new riverlet of muddy runoff. What was that!?

A single, plaintive k-lunk caught our ears. It took a little time of eye strain and horizon searching, but there they were. Two laggards were returning to the river. They gave forth an occasional k-lunk and were oh so high, but if they kept on course, they wouldn't miss us by too far. Out of sight behind the wall of our mud hole, I was fumbling for my call which we had had no occasion to use until now.

"Don't overcall," admonished Oley. The two birds were definitely river bound with outstretched necks giving the impression that were actually pulling the big bodies and acting as sensory devices for those powerful, pumping wings. I gave them my best staccato call and imagined at a quarter mile away, (they were missing us by that far) that I caught the lead bird's attention. I gave them another squank – my sweet call and tucked the Oldt down inside my coat. They were coming. In a wide sweeping circle, they set their wings and swung around to decoy. We were galvanized, hardly believing that we were about to get another, a second, chance this day. It didn't take long. We suddenly realized how fast they moved in their circle to come into the decoys, first over the two detached phonies, then as they were over the others, we realized they were also a bit beyond and that it was time to shoot. No spoken agreement was necessary – we had been here before shooting ducks. It wasn't necessary to discuss who took which bird. At the simultaneous crack of the guns, Oley's bird fell dead. Mine seemed to drop several feet, but instead of folding, recovered and set those wings in "sailing gear," which has lost many a bird for many a hunter. A split second of chagrin and despair went through me but somehow I kept my cool and that good old left barrel with a good lead, caused him to crumple and we had our four geese.

This last had taken place in a few seconds, in bright sunlight and not without a gallery – we knew there must have been a couple of hundred eyes watching our little drama.

We still had a decision to make. A five inch, wet snow, fast melting did not dictate that a soft stubblefield was any place to drive a light car with regular tires, so we packed out by towing the decoys sled-like, tied together to keep a compact cargo, 38 pounds of geese and all our equipment on a piece of tarp that really served double duty that day. Loaded in the car and finally back on the hiway, we looked at each other, laughed and almost in unison said "How about some dry food?" So, it was back to the cafe in Broadwater, where the waitress greeted us with "Well you guys had all the luck today, didn't you? How many did you get, four?" Well, that took all the surprise out of any modest announcement we might have been thinking about but it added another conclusion to our unusual day – don't ever underestimate the country party telephone line.

VIII

Watching the elderly Mexican mow my lawn and reviewing our steadfast relationship over past years, suggested to the writer that here was a good subject for a story. There were several well-thought-of Mexican families in his acquaintance that were good citizens. They raised their children in a creditable manner, paid their taxes and accepted the rules and ordinances which their caucasoid neighbors made (and sometimes broke) without complaint and so, we have the makings of a story— MANUEL'S MUSINGS.

Manuel's Musings

Old Manuel Valdez had never missed a day's work because of sickness, but now he was laid up indefinitely with a broken ankle. It had taken the impact of a heavy timber to crush the tough, wiry talus that had served him so dependably through most of his past 75 years.

Now he was sitting on his porch on a leather covered recliner chair, which one of the boys had acquired when a friend had discarded it because of its roughened appearance due to age and hard use. It had become Manuel's favorite and now he sat relaxed in it, with the injured foot in a raised position, while watching the pigeons darting here and there in the street in search of grain spilled from the loaded farm trucks enroute to the nearby elevator.

The old man had been born in a small poverty ridden village, somewhere in old Mexico. Alone, uneducated, but craving something better than the depressing promise his birthplace could offer, he emigrated to the United States at an age when his American counterparts had had a couple of years of high schooling and were more-or-less wise to the workings of this new country and its innumerable choices of future lifestyles.

Manuel's first employment was with a crew of his countrymen picking fruit or vegetables, whichever was in season. They were aliens of course, but the farmer boss had an investment to protect and paid little attention to their nationality or lack of citizen status. Manuel moved in any direction that required such seasonal labor and eventually he found himself aligned with a group of workers that moved to the sugarbeet fields of Colorado and western Nebraska.

This crop seemed to offer the nearest to continuous work throughout the growing season. First, came the thinning of the young plants. This was done with a hoe and the worker who's eyes could spot a *double* (two plants grown together so that the developed root or beet would be deformed and stunted) pleased the farmer. After the thinning phase was completed and settled for between the farmer and the crew boss, there was the hoeing—performed at a different rate of pay. It too was hot, hard work.

Then there was a period of unemployment until the harvest. This entailed topping the beets with a sharp, machete-like knife—cutting the leaves and stalk from the beet itself. The topped beets were then piled and loaded for hauling to a dump or factory. It was all backbreaking work and that interval between the hoeing and the topping meant unemployment and no pay, unless one had shown some aptitude for other work around the farm, moved to another part of the country temporarily to do field work, or was fortunate enough to find other work. This latter alternative was Manuel's good fortune and he found temporary work with a section gang on the railroad.

Here, working at an entirely different type of labor, he soon found himself in Alliance, Nebraska, which was an important division point on the Chicago, Burlington and Quincy railroad. Manuel was an apt student on those labor gangs. He soon learned never to be caught sitting down by the boss or the white-shirted office people – always be on the move, even at a slow pace, and always have something in one's hand – be carrying something. Such little things prevented a bawling out and made an impression.

It soon became apparent that Alliance was to be his home. The work was steady and there were others of his countrymen nearby and in the railroad's employ. Before long, it was only natural that Boy had met Girl – Manuel and Marie were married in a simple ceremony in the Catholic Church. There was a minimum of fuss with the affair, but both the bride and groom-to-be had made enough friends to make it an occasion to celebrate and an affair to remember. There was mucho vino, cerveza, food and music and a surprising number of well-wishing merrymakers. Some of those people even came from Scottbluff, a nearby town with an even larger Hispanic population.

The union was a good one from the start. Maria was a gentle person, a domestic houseworker who liked that association close to the wives of some of the influential white families in town. Here she had picked up many of the better things in American home life and culture. These sometimes differed greatly from that of her own people. Fortunately, she had been one who could pick out the characteristics that she wanted to build into her own family.

Manuel was a lucky man. Maria was a take-charge mate on the domestic side of their lives and that left him free to work. That was what he knew best – to get lost in his job, which involved him in a myriad back-breaking tasks. His lot was definitely manual labor. However, he also possessed another characteristic and that was to save. One didn't accumulate worldly goods too fast on a section worker's pay, but it was enough to satisfy their simple style of living.

It wasn't too long before they bought the little house which they had been renting. (That was when Manuel became acquainted with interest; before long he also learned about interest *received* and opened a small savings account with the bank). It is remarkable how this man, completely uneducated, learned to read, simple basic arithmetic and how necessary those two skills were to be in his life.

Their home was located near the railroad right-of-way with other Mexican families nearby. Manuel enjoyed that as it permitted him to visit and talk with his countrymen, but in the house, he required that English be spoken. A country that gave him so much deserved that its language be spoken in the home, although he was baffled and never did get it quite clear why the American language was called English. It was all right he guessed, inasmuch as the national leaders of the time freely accepted it. He did think that their bilingual tolerance was confusing and that the publishing of important notices and instructions, particularly at election time was an unnecessary concession to minorities, even the Hispanic portion of the population. His point of view in that respect was not always shared by his fellow Mexicans; but, he noticed that in spite of their attitude as a minority, few of them bothered to vote. The right to vote. That was a privilege that he and Maria cherished and exercised.

One of the first things he had aspired to do after he got his first steady job was to become a naturalized citizen. When his five years of residence was fulfilled he took that big step. It just wasn't right to partake of all the blessings (freedom) this new country gave him and not qualify himself to assume citizen responsibilities. He may not have expressed it in so many words that way, but he felt it and as time went by, he got that feeling across to each of the family.

Because Manuel was so serious about his patriotic responsibilities, someone presented him a plaque on which was printed one of the declarations included in an alien's petition for citizenship form:

"I am not a disbeliever in or opposed to organized government or a member of or affiliated with an organization or body of persons teaching disbelief in or opposed to organized government. I am not a polygamist nor a believer in the practice of polygamy. I am attached to the principles of the Constitution of the United States, and it is my intention to become a citizen of the United States and to renounce absolutely and forever all allegience and fidelity to any foreign prince, potentate, state, or sovereignty, and particularly to MEXICO to whom at this time I am a subject, and it is my intention to reside permanently in the United States."

It was given in a spirit of fun, possibly jest, but Manuel did not jest about that subject and the plaque was hung on the wall in a conspicuous location in the kitchen. Maria did not object and as time went on, it had a sobering effect on any reader. All the family read it and acquired a serious attitude toward their franchise.

Another personal characteristic in Manuel's make-up was that of inherent honesty. An example was the stack of used railroad ties

141

in his back yard. When the railroad section crews replaced old ties with new creosoted ones, the old ties might lay in the right-of-way for a period of time. Most of them were appropriated by farmers, fellow employees and others without permission or payment. Not Manuel — he had a creditable, neatly stacked pile of ties, which sometimes provided him a ready resale for a multiple use on the farms and ranches. He also had a receipt of payment for each one. Payment was made through the company freighthouse, probably at about twenty cents each to employees. Sam Cole, the railroad freight agent, was quick to notice Manuel's feeling of responsibility which was in contrast with many. Most standards of that early day did not regard stealing from the city or the railroad as a crime anyhow.

The old man was just beginning to doze as the review of and the self-satisfaction of such things lulled him into a state of torpor, when a clamor of a vehicle and the screeching of its tires coming to an abrupt stop brought him to his senses. Carlos was home! That's the way the young folks were — always in a hurry and so often, noisy about it. Carlos was the youngest son, and at age 16 possessor of a 1968 car. Briefly, Manuel contrasted such proprietorship with his own, or lack of any, at that age. The boy had dropped by to pick up something and then was off to football practice that seemed to have started before summer vacation was half over. Football and other sports were important phases of growing up with the boys. The other four had gone through it, and though Manuel was not one to mention it — they seemed to be turning out all right. A bit of pride surfaced here in him.

Now the girls were different. Only Izabelle, a senior in high school, seemed inclined towards participating in sports. A surge of tenderness flooded through him as he thought of the girls. They were so like his Maria.

Ah, that Maria. He recalled the day when she had accompanied Barbara to register for the first day of school. A nice lady, doing the same for a pretty little blue-eyed blonde girl, had been friendly to Maria just at the time when Maria was about to shrink to the rear of the line and escape any impending embarassment that never occurred.

"You'll just have to come to our first PTA meeting," the lady had said. "It is next Monday night, and all the mothers are expected to be there." Noting Maria's wariness about getting involved in something strange, she added, "You owe it to that cute little daughter — to know the program that the school system provides for our children."

Maria had wrestled with making a decision on whether or not to attend a meeting at which undoubtedly the important people of the town would be present and, would wonder about the presence of a mousey, half-scared little Mexican mother. A number of them did attend and she was surprised that she had been put at ease so easily. It seemed that all mothers had the same concern for their children. Mercy, she hoped there would not be great differences and that she would not have to take a stand on anything which she knew nothing about. Well, it had turned out great. Maria became a faithful attender at the meetings and the other women soon discovered that she was a tireless and willing worker.

Manuel smiled. He recalled being cajoled by the family to attend a covered dish PTA supper for the first time. That had meant dressing up – something the children had not seen before of him. It had apparently never been thought of. And, they actually seemed proud of the way he had looked – out of the loose-fitting work clothes, which were always clean enough due to Maria's efforts and care; but, what a contrast with the well-pressed blue serge suit covering the immaculate, slightly starched white shirt and a tie. Ah the tie, again he smiled remembering the quick search for that item, which had been overlooked completely in preparation for the big event. Finally a plain dark tie had been located in Roberto's room – one seldom worn by Roberto because it was too plain and drab. On Manuel it looked dashing and was really set off by that white shirt. Everyone had a part in getting Dad dolled up to go out. And in the end, everyone had been really proud that Dad was going out – taking Mother out for an evening with other townfolk. It had been a good experience and Manuel enjoyed it, even if he would not admit it.

The venture, a small matter to the average citizen who just took such things for granted, was one that led to his going out to more and other semi-public gatherings – especially if the proper or acceptable decor did not require that blamed tie.

The experience broke the ice for him to attend athletic events. Football and basketball he especially liked in the fall and winter months, when one of the boys might be playing. In the summer, he liked the Old Timer's City baseball program and seldom missed a game. All the boys had played baseball and he could attend those games. He wondered if young people in Mexico, south of the border, had anything comparable since he had left his homeland at that very age that he so enjoyed watching his own perform. Ah yes, his was a lucky lot. With closed eyes, he thought of the children.

Roberto had just completed medical school and was doing his residence requirements at an Omaha hospital before entering actual practice as a doctor. Some do it faster, but for the Valdez family, ⸀ it had meant seven years of frugal living and sacrifice.

Luis was through his schooling and was employed in one of those government services that so confused his father as to just what its function was, but Luis was good at helping his brother financially and he received a regular pay check. He also had to wear a tie. A faint smile spread over the old man's face just as Maria tiptoed through the door checking to see why things were so quiet. Characteristically, she likened that smile, which had softened the usually rugged but kind face, as similar to an infant's involuntary grimaces that usually followed overfeeding. Manuel was not used to being disabled and now had dozens of questions about the why of things that went on around the house. The things that were every day routine to Maria and the rest of the family, but for which he just naturally wasn't around enough to realize their existence. Quietly she retreated back into the house, a smile of understanding on her face. Let Dad dream.

Barbara, probably influenced by her two older brothers' chosen lots, was a registered nurse. Not too many of the influential parents could boast of three children in college at the same time. It hadn't been easy and it required many family sacrifices before she became a RN. Qualifying to wear that pin and that little cap cockily positioned atop her head became her pride and joy.

Nancy was an LPN. Family finances just wouldn't permit her attending college for the prestigious Registered Nurse status, but she hadn't given up on that and with brothers and sister working and bringing home paychecks, it would not be long, before she would have that opportunity, for together, they were a most close-knit family.

Dan was a mechanic. Apparently, he was a good one too because he had a following. One day he would be opening his own repair service. It was he who kept the 1972 station wagon and the pickup truck that Dad used for transportation to and from his lawn-mowing jobs around town, in running order. Since Manuel turned 65, an old man by the railroad company's standards, lawns and other yard work had been his livelihood.

Lupe was a salesperson in one of the ready-to-wear stores uptown. She learned quickly and was soon applying her buoyant personality to her job. Her boos was very pleased with her.

Carla was a beautician. The owner of the cosmetic parlor probably was influenced in hiring her because of her dark natural beauty that required no additives.

Angelo worked on the railroad. He had started as a laborer in the shops, but already had been promoted twice, and was the number

144

one helper in the diesel engine repair shop. His employment was the nearest to that of his Dad's original work with the railroad, except his lot required hard labor, grease and grime, whereas Manuel's was more likely to have combined hard labor, dust and grime.

Izabelle was a senior in high school. She was a bright student, and it was not without some semblance of truth, that she often had said setting a good example for Susan and Carlos sharpened her makeup and scholastic efforts. She participated in the girl's sports program too and was a stalwart on the volleyball team, having been mentioned on several all-conference teams and even mentioned for all-state.

Carlos was somewhere between a sophomore and a junior in high school. He was a good boy that was never in serious trouble, but somehow, class work in school had never bothered him too much. That car and whatever athletic program was in season captured all of his attention and most of his efforts. Maria had worried a bit about him in grade school, but realized that in a family of eleven children, they could not all be the same.

Susan was now in Junior High School, or Middle School, as the Board of Education had dubbed it defensively, while alluding to its original Junior High designation during the workup for the sale of bonds in a hotly contested local school improvement issue. She was Maria's last immediate reason for continuing in PTA, although she never quite understood all the arguments against the improvement program – it was for the good of the town's children. Susan was an active and energetic little girl. She seemed to have captured so much from the experiences of her older brothers and sisters, that scholastically, *she was way beyond her years*, as one teacher opined.

This sentimental wool-gathering was merging into a state of unconsciousness and a good nap, when Manuel had visitors. A police patrol car stopped in front of the house, and from it emerged the Police Chief and County Sheriff. Manuel, through the years, had nurtured a friendly relationship with law enforcement. Some of his neighbors didn't quite understand why their apparent friend was so cozy with police officers. Could it be that he was an informer?

Occasionally, both police and sheriff's departments needed an interpreter. Manuel was their man. Usually it was of a minor nature involving a migrant who couldn't read, much less understand, why he was out-of-step with the rules of the rest of society. Those were the easy cases. With an enterpreter, the unfortunate fellow received an explanation and instructions that he could understand.

Sometimes the transgressions were not that simple and charges and a court appearance resulted. The officers and the court had learned through experience that the pure castilian Spanish taught in school was more confusing to all parties than the Mexican dialect, which both the principal and interpreter understood. That was when Manuel was invaluable.

For most of his services, like the first example, where things were straightened out without any charge filed and a court appearance, his service was a gratus matter. If a more official handling was necessary, a fee for the enterpreter could be included in the court costs. Manuel understood this and the officers were appreciative of his willingness to help. It made for a happy arrangement for all parties, but that wasn't what had brought the officers this day.

This was a goodwill trip. They liked Manuel and having heard of his misfortune, they came calling. They took seats on the porch steps and after getting an account of the accident with genuine interest, shifted the conversation to a coming softball tournament, the cost of living, the standings of favorite baseball teams in the big leagues as the World Series dates approached.

Maria brought a pitcher of lemonade and glasses. She was greeted warmly, but did not remain long before reentering the house. She didn't wish to horn in on the man talk on subjects at which she was at a disadvantage. It was a nice visit and a delightful half hour. Then the visitors took their leave, jollying the old man and shouting a big "Thank You" through the screen door to Maria.

As they drove away, the sheriff said, "Cy, if all people in the world were like them, yes even the whole family, you and I wouldn't be needed and we'd be looking for other work." There was an "Uh huh" of agreement from the Chief.

Back at the house, Maria came out on the porch for the empty pitcher and glasses. "Those men are real friends," declared Manuel. "And thirsty ones," added Maria. They looked at each other and both broke out laughing.

* * * * *

Entering the Law Enforcement building, the two men separated to go to their respective offices, but not before the Sheriff observed, "That was a half hour well spent." The Chief answered, "Yeah, I feel good."

IX

One of my favorite stories is the memory of a very unusual hunt that I experienced as a youth under very unusual conditions. Well, you will just have to read the story of TEENAGE LUCK. RWL.

Teenage Luck

For some reason, school was dismissed for the afternoon. Lunch became a hurried thing and a hunt was planned immediately. Mom assembled the meal and I prepared for an afternoon on Bronco Lake. It would have appeared that I was going to stay for a week as I sacked the decoys, counted out my shells and set out the waders—just in case. I checked my gun several times and then gulped the lunch in spite of Mom's admonishment not to hurry. Then Pop came home.

He couldn't go for some reason or other, in spite of my invitation. Probably he thought it would be a waste of time with the hot, sunny day and the dry beastly wind.

"You want to take the car?" he asked.

"You bet!" I almost choked. That was the 1921 Ford touring car, with the isinglass side curtains in a neat roll and deposited under the cushion of the back seat ready for any emergency. I had sort of planned on using that car anyhow, but it was nice to have it suggested.

Then, "Would you like to take the automatic?" he asked.

Joy to the world! I had my first gun, a 16 gauge Stevens double barrel, which after many cans of 3-and-1 oil, administered with a flannel cloth and a jointed cleaning rod, shone inside and out from the meticulous care that goes with pride of owning a fine gun. But, although I had been so happy with that neat little gun for all of three years, recently I had coveted the idea of acquiring, somehow or other, a 12 gauge gun. After missing a shot, which was not an infrequent experience, I would have the urge for a larger gun. Of course Pop's automatic was my secret envy. Although I kept such wild and avaricious thoughts to myself helped by the thinking, also to myself, that someday that very "12" would become mine and that all those shots that its present owner made so expertly, would just naturally become mine. There would be no such thing as the human element and, the so-so marksmanship that I had evidenced so far in my hunting career, well that would just naturally be a thing of the past, with the demise of the little 16 double. I tried to hide my elation.

Pop was glad that I was hunting alone. He got out the well-cared-for automatic and going to the back porch, checked me out on its operation (just as I had done many times in private), like the safety, how to carry it and just how and when to push ahead that little metal block within the trigger guard and to carry it on "safe" at all times when I was not going to fire.

Then he said, "Now if you get an overhead shot coming at you, (I know he had little thought of getting such a chance on a sunny day as it was) get a bead on the bird, then gently bring the muzzle up and pull the trigger just as the sight raises to hide the target. Of course in this wind, you are more likely to get a passing shot with the bird going downwind. Then you want to lead Mr. Duck anywhere from five to twenty-five feet, depending upon the wind and how far away he is." Yes, yes, we had been over these little hints many times, but I was very patient.

I might say here that Pop was "Pop" to all of us, even my four aunts on Mom's side of the family. To his sisters, he was simply "Cy." Then he went back to work and I busied myself again checking shells. I had to rid my every pocket of the 16 gauge ammunition and count Pop's supply of "12s." I took plenty. Finally, I was on my way to Bronco Lake

Bronco Lake was only two and one-half miles from town. It was completely land-locked in a large basin – 246 acres of open water with 436 acres of marsh tailing off for a couple of miles west to the Snake Creek valley. Those are Soil Conservation measurements. It was so located on the flat tableland of the county, and laying like a mirror that it attracted any waterfowl that ventured down Snake Creek from the west or that came out of the famous Nebraska sandhills from the east. It was a dandy lake for hunting and was Pop's favorite – little wonder that I was almost 21 years of age before I realized there were other lakes and hunting in the country.

Bronco's marine life did not include fish because its water contained a high concentration of alkali and other salts, but it was a haven for ducks, both migratory and the home guards, as we called those staying through the summer. The latter were mostly puddle ducks making their homes in the marsh area during the nesting period.

From shortly after October 1 until the lake froze over in late November or early December, canvasback could always be seen "rafted up" in the center of the lake. That meant that they were "staying for dinner" for the vegetation that grew on the lake's bottom was tasty to their palates, particularly the bulb-like plant bearing the Indian name "wapati" – not the pronghorn animal.

Pulling into a parking place alongside the old scow, which Pop kept padlocked to the Country Club pier, I eyed the white caps on the lake proper and took note of the vicious northwest, 40 mile per hour wind that gusted at times up to fifty mph. It would be a challenge to get out on the lake and battle those big boiling crests and troughs across open water to where I hoped to set up for my hunt. For a moment I almost weakened as I visioned a wasted afternoon. I could have stayed home and worked a couple of pages of algebra and perhaps mastered one of those mean formulae that my math class was into at school. Then far out on the lake, something caught my eye.

A "Bull" Canvasback

At the moment, there was not a bird visible in the sky, but I saw the bright reflection of sunlight off the breast, sides and back of a, no several, canvasback drakes. Actually there was quite a concentration of cans. They were a massed flock heading into the wind and bobbing like corks as they attempted to ride the crests of the waves and then would disappear in the waves' troughs to reappear with the swell of the next white cap. It looked like a hopeless task swimming as they tried to make headway towards the outer reeds of the northwest part of the lake, behind where there would be quiet water.

That would be my objective. Should I take the decoys? Just as well, perhaps I could use them. They would be no help, if left in the car. So I packed them into the stern of the scow. There was plenty of room in that clumsy, 14 foot boat and the weathered gunnysacks they were in made really good camouflage. I placed the oars in their locks, checked the 12 foot pole that we often used instead of oars to push through rushes, loaded the automatic and laid it carefully across a sack of decoys handy to pick up and use if the occasion arose, and pushed off from the shore and began rowing.

My plan was to hug the north bank of the lake where the water was not as disturbed, and make for the lake's northwest corner. To cut across the open water would be foolhardy. I doubt if I could have held my own with those waves and the high wind. So I set a course quartering into the wind. This meant a longer route and more work, but with my bulky, unwieldy craft, I could make better time. I used this tacking procedure as my guide, watching the wake of the boat to tell if I was on course. The wake was short-lived and seldom visible for more than eight or ten feet before being swallowed up in the rampant churning of the angry water. After several minutes of this, I ventured a look out on the lake. I wanted to keep that raft of canvasback located. Low and behold, they were airborne and winnowing their way towards the outer rushes. Although scarcely off the water, they were making better time than when swimming.

Now I knew I was right. Whoops! I almost lost control as a gust of wind whipped my ungainly craft broadside. That was to happen more and more later in the afternoon. I concentrated on getting to the yonder side of a bay-like corner of the lake, where there would be shelter of sorts. Before long this came to pass and I lodged the scow in a patch of reeds, rested the oars alongside and huddled down out of the wind to recapture my breath and composure.

Scanning the down-wind area and the lake proper, I spotted part of the flock I was so fascinated with just beyond what appeared to be about a quarter mile of solid rushes. I was acquainted with the area and I knew there several patches of quiet water spotted irregularly throughout those reeds. Those cans knew it too. That was also their objective. When I finally quit trembling from excitement and exertion, I allowed the boat to drift broadside against a reef a rushes and carefully prepared for action.

I raised up slowly expecting a roar of wings to greet me. Frankly, I guess I was hoping that I was going to get a pot shot. Instead, all was quiet but there were a few birds in the air fighting to gain the quiet water. Then there were hundreds of them rising to clear the reeds bordering the open lake. I had misjudged how close they might be, but I guessed their line of flight perfectly. Dropping back down, I composed myself, flicked the safety trigger to the on position and waited.

The wait was not long, but in that brief span of time, I thought of mayhem I was capable of on those birds — today I had the 12! Then there they were in range — their big broad bodies, with the dark brown-reddish heads on straining necks and every part of their bodies streamlined in the effort to cut into the gale.

"Well don't wait all day!" I practically shouted aloud.

They were moving faster than I thought and if I had waited much longer, they would veer off and I would be left with that flairing passing shot that Pop had mentioned. I liked this chance much better and carefully drew a bead on a large drake that seemed to be the vanguard for those behind him. With the sight of his black breast, I raised the sight a mite and squeezed the trigger, just as Pop had instructed. There was a tremendous roar compared to a report from my little "16" and in the split second that followed, I saw my bird drop along with several others that had been tailing him.

"Well dummy, you have four more shells in the gun!" I thought and in that short time realized that most of the flock had not veered off or flared as one would expect. I guessed the effect of that vicious wind numbed their normal reaction. I methodically picked another target and got off the rest of the loads before the birds, now thoroughly confused, took off, caught the wind and winged back onto the lake.

I would never brag about it to Pop, or to some friends who had seen some displays of my marksmanship, but I had hit every bird that I had shot at plus a bonus of doubles or triples with a couple of the shots. Against the wind, they were hardly moving so it was just like shooting cans off the top of fence posts.

Like "shooting cans off a fence post"

"Well get busy boy or you'll be losing birds!"

I poled the clumsy scow through the rushes, and always battling the elements, finally picked up the last bird just before being swept from the protective cover of the rushes onto the angry rolls of waves

153

of greenish, gray lake water. Then getting back to my position broadside to the rushes, and probably two hundred yards from the open water, was no small chore. Again, I was exhausted, winded and glad for another opportunity to rest.

For the first time, I was able to count and admire the ducks I had picked up. I arranged them along the bottom of the boat and admired my kill. I had never bagged more than two canvasback before on a same day's hunt. Here there were ten – beauties all. I examined each one closely. The drakes were in prime plumage, but even the hens were pretty to me with their dull brown feathers flecked with silver. They were real northern birds, broad of breast and body, perhaps not as long as the old green head mallard, but just as heavy. Again I examined each bird to see if I had blown apart or ruined any of the several cripples that I had had to finish off. No, it was a fine collection – ten dead birds, none of them mangled from shooting too close.

Minutes had passed so I took a bearing on what had happened to the big flock. I finally located it far out in the open water, where it was going through the same hopeless battle with the elements.

In spite of the wind, there was other activity around the lake that day. There were quite a number of curious people visiting a new well-drilling site on the southwest side of the lake. The most direct route to this site was the two-rutted trail road around the east side of Bronco Lake. It was this automobile traffic that kept spooking my canvasback. From mid-lake, they would drift towards the east shore until discretion dictated that they again take to the air and fight their way westerly to the relatively quiet back water and shelter from the wind. This little game, a choice between the annoyance of gas driven engines and battling the elements, was being repeated all afternoon.

Again, I was about to get another chance. I noted a repeat performance by the big flock, flying about four or five feet above the water and headed directly for me. Again, I "shot cans off the top of fence posts," but not to down ten ducks this time. However, it was no easier to recover three or four birds and then battle my way back to my hiding spot. We repeated the performance three more times and I had "my" limit – 20 canvasback. Not a teal, ruddy or trash duck in the bunch – just a straight canvasback kill.

It was time to call it quits and figure out how best to take advantage of the wind and return to the pier. There was no real problem in this except with the continual splashing of the waves against the side of the scow, I was pretty well drenched by the time I reached shore. Then it was a matter of transferring all of the useless, unused decoys, extra shells, boots and paraphernalia from boat to car. A couple of gunnies were just right for the game and then I was homeward bound, where I soon arrived, proud as a peacock and maybe just a little bit cocky. I knew a dozen guys that would have been on Bronco Lake that afternoon had they any notion of what was taking place there.

Once home, I unloaded the car near the back porch and entered the house rather nonchalantly but wise enough to combine entrance with a little thoughtfulness by gathering up several newspapers which I spread over an area on the back porch to receive the contents of the gunnysacks. Mom was busy in another part of house, but hearing me bump around the kitchen and porch, greeted me with, "Well, did you have any luck?" and then she saw that pile of ducks on the porch floor.

"Oh Bob, what will your dad say when he sees that?" She was used to bags of game, in all sizes, "and, they're all alike! Canvasback aren't they?" She was like that – always interested in our luck. "Thanks for spreading the papers."

"What will we do with them?" she had become as excited as I was. "You know the ice box won't hold that many."

"Now just a minute Mom," I said. "I have a plan. Do you have any paraffin left from canning?" She did, and we embarked on a great experiment.

I had witnessed parts of the new process at an old colored woman's place where we sometimes took our game to be dressed, when we were too tired or had other things to do. It involved cutting off the wings and head of the bird, rough picking the breast and some of the back and side feathers and then dipping the bird, completely submerging it in a pail of scalding water containing the melted paraffin. Holding the bird by the feet, it was possible to swirl the half-picked body gently so that the hot oil encased every pin feather, down and even some of the courser feathers. After cooling, which caused the paraffin to congeal and harden around every feather, it was a simple matter to peel off the wax. The feathers came with it and presto – we had a cleanly picked bird.

Mom was delighted with the end result. Pop usually supervised the picking phase – the distasteful part of our sport, but his methods were of the "Old School" and entailed laboriously dry-picking the duck and then singeing the pin feathers and fine down over a flame – usually a torch of twisted paper. The stench of burned feathers was terrible and that phase should have been performed out-of-doors. Quite often it was not. Then the whole house became permeated with the stench of burned feathers.

No wonder Mom was ecstatic. What a saving on her housekeeping! She was actually willing after this demonstration to bend the

rule, her rule of "you clean the game you get and I'll cook it, but . . . "
She was now fascinated with this "new to us" method that she entered
into the chore with almost girlish enthusiasm. We didn't have too
much wax so we did six birds, about what the ice box would hold,
and stopped.

I had in mind giving the remaining 14 ducks to friends and
neighbors after Pop came home and saw what I had done that afternoon with his automatic. It wasn't long before he did arrive. I barely
had time to clean the gun. It was spotted and streaked with alkali
spray, now dried, and the grime from resting across dirty gunnysacks.
By the time he entered the house though, it was clean – lightly polished with gun oil and the inside of the barrel glistening.

Pop was impressed, and then like he always was wont to do,
he squatted down by that pile of ducks and examined each one.
He was finally satisfied and convinced that I hadn't "Arkansawed"
the bunch of them by the way the shot entered their bodies. He
looked approvingly at the six fat bodies we had "picked" and then
he took over the butchering. He received no argument from me on
that. Whether it was by design or not, he was busy with his self-
appointed chore and I was going out of my mind at his lack of
interest in all the details of my hunt, which I was bursting to tell.

In time I was given that opportunity and I guess that was
for the better for then, through with his butchering, he lit up a
fresh cigar and listened. He was as interested in my afternoon experiences as if he had been along to share them. Then, as I sort
of wound down on my relating events of the hunt, he began to
participate and the talking drifted into a discussion of canvasback.

A third pair of ears was taking in all of this man-talk. Meanwhile, Mom also busied herself with supper preparation and other
domestic chores, but I would warrant that had she suddenly been
confronted with a pop quiz on the subject, Mom would have turned
in a creditable grade on the subject of hunting and wildlife. Needless
to say, I was blessed with a very, very exceptional pair of parents.

The topic of discussion became *canvasbacks*. The hunter-reader
in some areas of the country – coastal waters or larger lakes with
their favorite passes still provide the occasional sight of a flock of
"cans" swinging by with jet-like speed and precision may wonder
why this duck is held so high in our esteem. Well, I guess the answer
to that is that we are natives to the lake country of the Nebraska
sandhills, which once boasted of a very busy, crowded flyway which
furnished many enviable and breath-taking flights of this noble bird.

I feel very fortunate to have hunted before this grand bird, the
canvasback, dwindled in population to a point of near extinction.
It is quite possible that many hunters of another, future generation

may never see a canvasback because they are not a duck to survive in public parks.

* * * * *

It is a sad commentary on man's conservation efforts that agricultural progress, particularly pump irrigation with its mining of our underground water supply, must have such negative effects on wildlife habitat. Bronco Lake, which in earlier years, measured to depths of eight and ten feet in many places, has been completely dry for more than 20 years. Its marsh is now spotted with hay stacks and the basin of the lake proper is foul ground, trashy with weeds and is an annual challenge to its several owners in their futile efforts to coax forth a decent crop of small grain.

X

Thinking that the SMORGASBORD should have a bit of fiction in it, the NIGHT ON THE TOWN has been included. It is not altogether fiction as there is considerable reminiscence included. In recalling English Professor Wimberly's classroom example of the difference between a comedy and a tragedy, the story would classify as a tragedy as *Boy did not get girl.*

Night on the Town

Late January in Lincoln, Nebraska, was not that college town's claim to greatness. But, it was late January in the mid 1920's.

The sharp northwest wind was cruel. It was also the semester break. Some students had completed their final exams, for better or worse. Others were lost in worried study for tomorrow's tests. The weather was grey, wintry and of little or no encouragement.

Downtown the bitter, cold wind of the grey day challenged the shopper and bit into the exposed legs of the flapper coed, protected only by the thinnest rolled-down hose – a forerunner of the bare-legged bobbysoxer. It was just so downright unpleasant that girl-watching at the intersection of Thirteenth and O Streets was at a complete standstill.

Only the movie houses or a basketball court (indoors) offered any time-killing possibilities. Within the fraternity house some horseplay might be generated, but even there, there was a subdued atmosphere hanging over the place out of respect for some last minute studying by the poor devils reviewing for the 'morrow. The volume on the Orthophonic record player was toned down.

Dejectedly, I parked the car; gave a cursory glance to the collection of vehicles already home, concluded it was to be another unexciting winter night and entered the fraternity house. Almost at once I was greeted with, "Here's Laing. He'll go." A couple of the brothers were trying to get up a group to go to Omaha. Harry Wilder had a new car and they were just dying to help him put a few miles on it.

Wilder was not unwilling for Omaha promised a complete change of atmosphere. It had all the attractions of a big city – shows, dining places, bright lights, and all the tinsel characterizing the metropolitan answer to the country's great social experiment – prohibition. Of course, it was the prospect of spiking a little booze or quaffing some homebrew in one of the many speakeasies in the big town that excited the fellows. The possibility of such an evening in Lincoln with its blue law reputation was practically nil, and the boys were definitely in a mood to unwind. I played hard-to-get, but not for long.

The sixty mile trip was uneventful except for light-hearted conversation. As we came nearer our objective, eating seemed a popular idea, and something should be secured with which to spike a soda before eating. This was no problem.

Wilder knew the area and after a brief stop at a certain filling station, somehow came up with a bottle of hooch.

The Virginia was a popular cafe in Omaha, especially to the young visitor, as in *Nebraska University Undergraduate*. So the Virginia it was. Setups were ordered and we placed our orders.

Although a pint of booze wasn't too effective when shared by five youth, it did seem to warm the body and spice the conversation. In fact, all became quite garrulous as not one was a practiced drinker. It was fun and harmless. The food was good and the management obliging. Somehow it was satisfying to the ego to be seen by one's peers in such circumstances – there were several other tables seating faces familiar to the campus in Lincoln.

When our repast was finished, we paid our bill, including a gratuity, which was not a too well established practice in those days, especially with students, and ambled out of the place with an air of worldliness.

Not too far away was a public dancehall by name of The Roseland. While in the neighborhood, the five adventurers decided to look in upon it and see what it had to offer.

The dancehall comprised the second floor of some sort of retail store and one entered from the side street through a wide opening to a stairway. As we approached to enter, there was a commotion at the foot of the stairs. The doors opening onto the sidewalk burst open from the impact of a man's body as it hurtled down the stairs onto the sidewalk, where he righted himself, apparently unhurt.

He attempted to dust off his clothing, but any further thought he may have had about personal appearance was ignobly thwarted by a tirade of threats from the irate bouncer, who followed him down to the bottom of the stairs.

I gasped because I recognized the poor fellow as an acquaintance from my home town. The hackles on my neck bristled and my first impulse was to go to the fellow's assistance, but he took one look at the bouncer, concluded that he was not welcome and made his way down the street staggering, not as much from his rude exit as from his drunken state. I thought better of making myself known. We entered the stairway and ascended to the dancehall properly impressed that intoxication was frowned upon here in no uncertain terms. That bouncer was a big man!

The dancehall was jumping with activity. The area near the top of the stairway was crowded with stags. Whether these people, mostly men, had any idea of dancing or not, I couldn't determine, but I concluded that most of them were ready for anything.

This area was separated from the dance floor proper by an effective barricade of fencing – roping supported by heavy pedestals. There was a booth from which this roped area seemed to pivot to admit

162

the dancers to the floor with surprising efficiency. This pivot point also served when reversed – to clear the floor at the end of each dance.

At the booth a pin and ribbon for the coat lapel was sold for general admission along with individual dance tickets to be collected from each entry to the roped area. Men were buying tickets, usually in a skein of five or ten, and then looking speculatively around the hall for a partner. I recalled a popular song with a sensitive, plaintive theme, *Ten Cents A Dance*.

The short interval between dances was broken by a burst of instrumental fanfare ahead of the next selection. That got my attention and I looked over at the band. "Not bad," I thought. It consisted of some ten musicians and was well balanced instrumentally. Since most of my college was being financed by playing for dances, I was combining a critical ear on the music and an eye on the band members for possible recognition of any of the players. Sure enough, I spotted a fellow, Randy Johnes, in the saxophone section. His face lit up with recognition and he waved me to come over. I would have to cross over an area of the dance floor to do that – something I was a bit reluctant to do without a partner or permission, but the man taking tickets and manning the ropes had witnessed Randy's gesture and he nodded permission. I went to the bandstand.

I had played a few jobs with Randy and I noticed that he had a few words with the leader, who looked my way and smiled a welcome. Later, he came over to the edge of the bandstand where Randy and I were visiting between sax passages, was quite cordial and asked if I'd like to sit in. This was practically unheard of unless one was established and expected. I looked at Randy. He had a smile on his face and quickly became busy with his orchestrations.

"Well, I do happen to have a mouthpiece with me," I answered, "but I'll have to take leave of my friends first."

"Anytime," he said.

I rejoined the fellows and explained to them and to Harry in particular, the circumstances and that I'd like to stick around and play with this band. This was all right with them as they were more interested in getting on their way to patronizing a couple of the many "Jack's places" that south Omaha boasted of and, drink some homebrew.

"I'll be here, or if it's after closing time, I'll be waiting at the Virginia," I told Harry.

"Okay," he agreed, "Give 'em hell." Harry was a good friend and he understood my strong leaning towards music and orchestra work.

I listened for a few minutes concentrating on the music. These guys were pros! In addition to handling in an expert manner the standard Jenkins and Fiest orchestrations, which I had noticed on

163

their music racks, they "cut the mustard" dictated by the written arrangements with a catchy style and smooth harmonizing. The slick saxophone section produced a pleasant woodwind drone to be punctuated by the brass background, all accompanied solidly by the very able pianist, flashy drums and the regular plinkety-plink of the banjo.

I was particularly impressed by the trumpet player, Ducky Drake, probably because I would soon be playing alongside of him and blending the trombone, more or less, with his trumpet. He had a flaring style, which was in itself a challenge. His playing reminded me of a jam session I had heard once, when Muggsy Spanier, with Joe Bushkin at the piano, stopped the show with their fox trot and ragtime renditions. I was impressed and ready.

I don't think this orchestra had a name. It just played at the Roseland. Therefore it was The Roseland Band. Omaha boasted of many dance bands. I was familiar with (Art) Randall's Royal Orchestra, which usually played at the Fontenelle Hotel ballroom; and with Cogwell's College Club bunch made up mostly of medical students. They played most of the fraternity and sorority dances. Then there was an individual from North Dakota by the name of Lawrence Welk, who always seemed to be turning up with his accordian and a pretty fair bunch of musicians.

No one seemed to know whether Welk was going to make it big in music or head up a big chicken and egg conglomerate from his little hatchery in west Omaha. He was considering such a business in order to spend more time with his family. Looking back, I'm glad the chicken business didn't work out because in music, his name has become a household word all over the country.

Making my way across the now crowded floor, I stood by the bandstand for a few minutes until Jim, the leader, saw me. Then I accepted his invitation to step up on the bandstand and was given a seat alongside the trombonist. He was a friendly sort, which relieved me. Sometimes a musician can be a little touchy about having a stranger invited to substitute in his stead. However, Gib, as everyone called him, was about to take a vacation. As he fully intended to return and have a job after three or four weeks absence, he was more than agreeable to my substituting. This also explained why the leader had welcomed me. Randy, bless his heart, had put in the good word for me.

Gib was generous about my using his horn and smiled with understanding and approval as I produced my own mouthpiece. I took his chair, tried the slide of the horn, blew any remaining saliva (spit to a player) from it and I was ready.

It was a most enjoyable hour. They had a variety of popular tunes, most of which were familiar to me. As the band and the leader became used to me, I was given the opportunity to solo and take an occasional break. Breaks were quite in vogue in the 1920's and hardly a fox trot or one step was played without the band building up to a crescendo, whereupon one player was given the opportunity to improvise several measures. It sounds easy but regardless of how wild a break an instrument took, its owner was expected to return to the melody or theme with a smoothness as if it was so written.

As I recall, *Tea for Two, Whispering, Dinah, Blue Skies, Margie, Avalon, Some of These Days*, and even, *Paddlin' Madylin Home*, along with a few waltzes like *Always* and *Charmaine* were some of the selections played in that all-too-short period. I was impressed with the band and the dancers accepted its offerings with enthusiasm.

One thing about the program that struck me was the sameness of it all. The band played a couple of numbers; the dancers then were practically herded off the floor and to the sidelines. They accepted such treatment, but to me it seemed a bit monotonous. I thought dancing should be more of a romantic adventure than a program of sameness.

Gib returned from somewhere and claimed his horn and place with the band. I sat and visited with Randy for a little while. The leader came over and observed, "You fitted in real nice. Interested in a couple of weeks work with us?" I told him I was a student and with the beginning of a new semester, couldn't take on something that steady. He seemed to understand and agree; but believe me, I felt flattered and told him so. So much for my evening's experience with the Roseland Band as a musician.

Leaving the bandstand, I spent a couple of tickets dancing with "taxis." These girls seemed in abundant supply for the men stags and were willing partners, but for the most part they entered into their work almost mechanically and without enthusiasm. They could all dance adequately. They had to manage with the variety of partners they drew throughout the evening. One "leader" might be a smooth dude expecting the girl to follow his version of Fred Astaire; the next partner could be a rough, stomping and sometimes pawing type with little natural rhythm. Usually there was little conversation and they gave the impression that it was just a job and I guess for them it was. They were usually sweaty from their last go-round, their clothes wrinkled from the exercise and the aroma of a cheap perfume blended with the odor of a perspiring body was a welcome addition. Oh well, every job has its drawbacks. Maybe I was too particular.

I had just finished a dance, when I noticed a girl picking her way through the thinning crowd "being herded" from the dance area. She headed straight for the man taking tickets and manning the rope.

This girl had a freshness in her appearance—both in physical features and dress. Her step was brisk with a swinging gate that was almost a glide. Every moment suggested youth. Her face was beautiful and intelligent looking; her dress was simple yet styled with clever tailoring to accent, without overdoing things, an ample blouse, and a slender waist atop a swishy, knee-length (I think) skirt. Below the hem of the skirt was a shapely calf and ankle in real sheer hose (silk I guessed) and with slipper-like shoes that bespoke exquisitely good taste. I was impressed! I had to have a dance with that person.

She was still talking to the floor manager and they both laughed and exchanged pleasant conversation. I hated that he should engage this gorgeous creature for so long. Then his duties drew him a few feet away from her as his attention was directed to some little problem on the floor. That was my chance.

"Like to dance?" I ventured.

She turned, curious at the interruption and cast an appraising but not unfriendly glance upon me. I felt that it took in, in one swift moment, my height, weight, dress and an analysis of any wolfish inclinations. Apparently I passed inspection.

"In just a moment," she replied. "I have something unfinished with Al."

"I'll be back in a moment," I said. "As soon as I get another ticket or two."

I brought forth a dollar at the booth, pocketed my skein of ten, and returned to the girl. Al gave me a quizzical glance but said nothing. Apparently, they had finished their conversation and we were free to dance.

I was amazed!

The other girls were good dancers and could follow. As said before, it was expected that they should be; but this girl, Frances, was something else. Every step became a glide, as if practiced. My every lead and move was predetermined and mutually favorable to each partner. We moved as one—smooth, graceful and with a mutual confidence in each other's concept of matching the best of music with our steps and maneuvering among the other dancers.

This was an exciting experience. We headed toward the center of the floor where it was better lit and not quite as crowded. Other couples soon discovered this and as these dancers moved in, our freedom on the floor was reduced. Then I noticed the corners of the hall were not lit so brilliantly, although they were not dark.

The crowd seemed to avoid these areas. I headed for a corner and found my partner equally able and willing to maneuver our way through the crowd with a minimum of bumping, barely brushing other dancers. There was no stumbling or faulty stepping that might have come from indecision between partners. Now we had more room and freedom to execute a few intricate steps with a moderate amount of whirling to make the fox trot a bit more interesting.

I think the girl had been testing too. She probably concluded that, "Here is a guy who likes to dance. He has the urge to attempt some fancy stuff, but not the nerve to try it. He does have a natural rhythm and a grace of movement that makes him interesting. I don't think he's a wolf so if I'm going to be dancing tonight, I could do a lot worse."

Of course, I wasn't in on her inner thoughts, but things were working out so beautifully that I didn't care at the time. It was recalling these events and the review of the evening on the return trip to Lincoln that pumped up my own conclusions and warmed my ego.

Damn, things were going well! I had never had any dance instruction, but had the conviction that it was the man's responsibility to lead. At that I was adequate but very conservative, when it came to trying new steps. Then unconsciously, we broke into what I learned later, the professionals called a lock step – sort of a quick side stepping action, where my right foot and her left crossed quickly and then reversed the action as our opposite feet automatically stepped into place. I had never had the nerve to try that myself, although I had seen it executed many times on the dance floor while I would be playing. This accidental entry into the maneuver was so successful and easy that somehow I swung her into a presentation position after a more or less clumsy (on my part) ronda to a slip pivot maneuver. Verily, this was a most pleasant and triumphant experience!

The success of our maneuvering now permitted further assessment of each other. Her left hand rested comfortably at the base of my collar but was by no means grasping. I tingled with gratification for that. I pressed her waist slightly, not that it was necessary to secure the magic of our dancing address – it was more of a gesture of gentle reassurance that I felt comfortable with her. She cast an inquiring glance at me, as if to determine my intentions, but did not become tense or pull away. I guess my involuntary action passed her appraisal.

Her face radiated her enjoyment of dancing. I can say that was mutual. We were more than just compatible. She was not breathing with any effort from exertion of our dancing, which caused me to

wonder about her presence here. She had appeared at a time when the evening had progressed. She seemed to have the stamina for the full evening but then, this was her first dance. Her eyes were laughing and flashing with enjoyment – I started to say excitement, but she seemed so composed that I chose a different word.

Now the music stopped but started up again almost immediately. The dances continued to be run off like clockwork. In the pause, giving us barely time to release each other from the standard embrace required in close dancing, I caught the flash of rings on her third finger. She intercepted my glance and impishly awaited my reaction.

I wasn't about to show any feeling or surprise. I took her hand and with my thumb on the rings asked, "Is he here?" Her "no," was in a playful, almost saucy vein.

Momentarily, I had thought that the floor manager might have been her husband.

"But he will be here shortly after eleven," she added.

I thought it not too wise, or tasteful, to press for further information about the husband. He was a lucky fellow. I was having fun and she seemed to be enjoying things. It was all harmless pleasure and such a pleasant experience of the evening was not going to be dampened by any *faux pas* on my part. We kept on dancing. Somehow, we were never "herded" from the floor as were the other dancers, therefore my supply of tickets was hardly diminished. We talked about many things. Everything seemed to develop and take place so easily. I became aware that this girl was an artist at getting to the nub of things – she was learning more about me than I was about her.

We talked about university life and, "Damn!" she drew me into that. I wanted to learn more about her. That was soon to happen.

After we had made a number of circuits around the floor, the band leader suddenly caught my attention. His motion invited us toward the bandstand, but his interest was in Frances.

"Want to sing a couple?" he asked her to my surprise.

"Oh all right," then impishly, "If Mr. Laing doesn't object."

"Well hell, he shouldn't object. He was up here himself a while ago." That, of course, surprised the girl as she had entered on the scene shortly after my stint with the band.

I waited patiently, very curious and visiting now and then with Randy while Frances sang. I wished I could have had her in my arms during each piece. She was great!

I recall several of the songs, but particularly remember *Always*, a waltz in a touching sentimental manner, *Manhattan Serenade*, belting out that fox trot with a plaintive, throaty feeling. Then for an encore, the band launched into *Dancing With Tears In My Eyes* featuring her singing the chorus:

"For I'm dancing with tears in my eyes
" 'cause the girl in my arms isn't you
"I'm dancing with somebody new –"

whereupon she turned and cast me a quick, teasing glance as if the song's words were meant for us.

There was just a little extra touch in her delivery of the song without any hitch in the lyric, but it did not go unnoticed by some of the band. They laughed and, I think with some degree of envy, kidded me with some pointed remarks.

"The little flirt!" I thought, and later asked her if that little incident was part of her usual routine, to which she merely wrinkled her nose without an intelligible answer.

When she finished, the applause from the dancers expressed approval of a job well done. The fellows in the band gave her a hand too. Her popularity was so obvious that when I claimed her for dancing, it was with some little self-consciousness. We danced away and were both silent for a little while.

Then, "Damn!" I broke the silence, "You were really good!" "You had a surprise for me too," she replied. "Jim said that you worked in real smoothly with the band."

I thought I felt a little tightening of her hand and arm on my shoulder, so I responded with a slight pressure in my clasp around her waist. Neither spoke for a little while. Lost in our own thoughts, we just danced.

I couldn't help analyzing our dancing. I felt just like a Fred Astaire no less. Although unrehearsed, our every movement was smooth and effortless. I couldn't help thinking as we might be in a fan and swivel maneuver, with a modicum of posing by Frances during a turn, that our free-flowing exhibition was almost professional instead of merely social dancing.

Then we danced past the floor manager, who was preparing to do his little "herding" chore. He cautioned, "Ah, Ah, be careful, Francie." We both laughed, realizing there was some sentimentality entering into our dancing. This could have been noticeable to anyone interested enough to watch. It did serve to bring us back to reality.

"Well, there's John," she said after a little. "Probably a good thing that he finally showed up."

I followed the direction that she was looking to see a nice looking fellow coming into the hall through the standing crowd. His eyes were searching the dancers on the floor. Then he saw us and a smile broke across his face. For some reason, I steered our course to the sidelines nearest him without so much as a suggestion to do so from Frances.

"You're a little late tonight," she said, but without any reproach whatever and then, "John, this is Bob Laing. We've been having some pretty nice dancing and a couple of surprises. I'll tell you about them later."

John's handclasp was firm and warm. I liked him immediately, but I hadn't figured out yet their strange relationship. I felt that had our positions been reversed, I'd have been dancing with my wife. However, his attitude or bearing did not indicate any guilt or feeling of neglect—only a tacit acceptance of the circumstances in their lives. Frances seemed to go along with his attitude and mode for living. His question, now directed to her, momentarily puzzled me.

"How is everything going?"

"Okay, Al has a little problem with the janitor,'" she answered with amusement. Apparently there existed a slight difference of opinion between the two men on the extent of the janitorial duties.

"I think that is going to be a continuous thing and you had better get Mrs. Jenkins before she gets tied up with something else."

"Jim wants to talk with you about those two irregular dates coming up, and I guess that's about all."

I listened patiently. The music stopped and the dance floor had cleared. Al was again admitting dancers onto the floor. John excused himself and proceeded toward the bandstand, then stopped and returned to us.

"Bring him over to the apartment afterwards, if you'd like," indicating me with a reassuring smile that I wouldn't be waylaid or anything for entertaining his wife. We've got company showing up about then."

I knew that a visiting delay after this dance was not a practical thing with Harry Wilder and the brothers expected back at any time, but the apartment John had referred to was just in the next block. I was so curious that I accepted. It was midnight now and the bad was playing *Home Sweet Home*. I walked along with Frances and John and we were soon joined by two couples whom I met but whose names I never will remember.

Shortly, I learned that John was a technician and frequently worked late in a brightly lit laboratory a short distance from their home and the Roseland. The Roseland, by the way, was leased and managed by John and Frances. Well, that accounted for a lot.

One bottle of the best home brew that I ever had tasted, and I just had to take my leave. John insisted on driving me to the Virginia, only a few blocks away. After checking inside of the restaurant and finding no trace or report of my party, we sat in his car and talked.

Of course he was interested in me, in my school, the courses I was taking, my activities and even my home; but he also was primed to talk about himself and the wife, who had been such a charming companion to me that evening. This was great. I gathered they were very much in love, living a strange life perhaps, but in complete agreement and trust. He was working on his first ($) million, as he lightly put it; she was in complete agreement with making the domestic sacrifices required to accomplish his ambitions. The dance hall was a second income. He impressed me as being extremely intelligent and that he must have been very capable in the demanding work at the laboratory.

Shortly, Harry Wilder drove up and scanned the restaurant for me. I hailed his attention and his wait was very brief while I said my goodbyes to John, and we were off to Lincoln.

I was thankful for a rear seat in the car because that permitted me to think. The funseekers soon sacked out, but poor Harry, who was probably as tired and sleepy as anyone, steered a careful course home.

What of my night? Certainly it was unusual and exceptional. I snuggled down in the collar of my top coat and considered things. Monday would be school again. Should I attempt to duplicate the Roseland experience along with my college work? Should I attempt to see Frances again? I thought of our movements on the dance floor, our mutual rhythm with the music, the gentle pressure of her hand in mine, the sensational fragrance of her perfume, the playful impishness in her teasing and the satisfaction and lift that her tolerance to some of my witticisms gave me. Seeing her again was a most desireable challenge, but what of my own personal life? I had responsibilities and debts. Ah yes, debts. That thought of paying off some borrowed money was a sobering one. Whereupon my mental wanderings drifted off into sleep.

The next thing I knew, Harry announced, "Well, here we are — home."

Sunday was a lazy day. Of course some sort of report on the big night in Omaha was expected of the funseekers and no little imagination and bravado was expressed by four members of the party, but not from the fifth. I couldn't risk telling about my night at the Roseland. No one would have believed me. I could imagine the hoots of derision that would have been given my tale, if it was truthfully related. I couldn't face the jeers that would have been given my naivete. Hell, it was none of their business anyhow.

Monday classes took up for the new semester and I received calls to play of couple of dance jobs over the weekend. There were new books to buy and supplies to acquire along with taking care of a bank overdraft. How could a student take care of all those things and add time-consuming activities that might turn out entanglements?

* * * * *

Time flew by and it was fully two months later when I had an opportunity to be in Omaha. Not that I ever dismissed the memory of my night at the Roseland — I don't think that will ever happen. What a shock — the dancehall was operating, but under new management. The orchestra had disbanded — only two fellows of the old Roseland band were now playing there and they knew nothing of Frances or John. I received the *"John who?"* treatment at the laboratory from people on the day side of that operation. The landlord of their apartment was out of town so I learned nothing there. The whereabouts of my new friends of such brief duration remains a mystery yet today. Occasionally, I run across a partially used skein of tickets that I had found in my coat pocket later so I know I'm not dreaming. The experience remains as a souvenir in my memory.